My Wife in Bangkok

by

Rory O'Merry

ASIA PRESS
Berkeley, California
1990

Photographed, Written and Designed by Rory O'Merry.

Edited by Claire Burch

Library of Congress Cataloging-in-Publication Data
O'Merry, Rory, 1948 -
  My wife in Bangkok / Rory O'Merry.
      184 p.   5 1/2" x 8 1/2"
  I. Title
  PS3565.M47M9   1990   89-18285
  813'.54--dc20   CIP
  ISBN 0-9625048-0-7

For information contact:

ASIA PRESS
P.O. Box 5446
Berkeley, CA 94705-0446

Printed by Thomson-Shore, Inc.
P.O. Box 305
Dexter, Michigan 48130-0305

Manufactured in the United States of America

TABLE OF CONTENTS

The face of time in Bangkok.

INTRODUCTION

Thailand, the Land of Smiles. It entertains over four million tourists a year and over 70% of these tourists are men. They come from all over the world, many of them drawn not only by the beautiful *wats* (temples) but by the availability of the women. The number of women who sell their bodies has been estimated at as high as 500,000, but even this is probably a conservative figure. In Thailand, you can rent a woman by the hour, by the week, by the month. In fact, you can purchase a Thai wife. They're not expensive.

The evolution of the sexual service industry is a direct result of a number of historical, economic and social factors. The presence of foreign troops in Asia during a succession of wars is probably responsible for its present-day form.

2

On the one hand, there is a poverty-stricken rural population, on the other, a society that stresses the lowly economic and social role of women. For most of these women the only way to earn a decent living wage is by migrating to the capital and becoming a prostitute, even though prostitution was formally outlawed in 1960.

The result is a tourist industry that generates 1.5 billion dollars a year. Welcome to Bangkok, the Angel City, the capital of Thailand. It is home to approximately five million people. The total population of Thailand is 50 million.

The government of Thailand is a bicameral parliamentary system, with a 100-seat appointed Senate and a House of Representatives, which has at least 240 seats. The present king, Bhumipol Adulyadej (Rama IX), is a constitutional monarch. He is loved and respected by the people. In fact, any act that might be regarded as *les majeste* is a criminal offense.

The state religion is Theravadin Buddhism and it is practiced by about 90% of the population. The national language is Thai.

Thailand, Land of Smiles. A construction worker still manages a smile after a day's work carrying cement for 80 baht. She could have earned 500 baht downtown for 20 minutes work.

Chapter 1:

HOW I MET PIDANG

Armed with this information and with a few other facts — one dollar is approximately 25 *baht* — hot season from March through May, rainy June through October, cool November through February — I arrived in Thailand on December 20. The taxi driver took me from one hotel to another, telling me they were all full. Finally he found one that would give him a big enough cut of the 500 *baht* (about $20) I was to pay for one night. The place was a dump. I cleared out the next morning and checked into a guest home near the National Library, where a dorm room cost me 50 *baht*.

I'm a freelance photojournalist. I had a photography project in mind — so I went to the World Fellowship of Buddhists building on

Sukhumvit Road. They gave me a guide called *Meditation Temples in Thailand.* Now that I was actually in the Far East, somehow this all seemed very depressing, so I went for a walk. I wound up in a place called the Bier-Kutsche, an open-air bar on Soi 3, opposite the Grace Hotel.

It was three days before Christmas: the busy season for the prostitutes. Nevertheless, there were at least 100 women sitting around the bar and only 70 or so men, mostly English and German.

A woman caught my eye and smiled. I smiled back. Her smile was to let me know I could go over and talk to her. If we liked each other — or if I just wanted to go to bed with her — and the price was right, off we'd go. If we got on well after the first night, we might stay together for the duration of my holiday (the average tourist stays five days) or until my money ran out. All I'd have to do is maintain the lady in the fashion to which she's accustomed.

A sort of temporary wife. Only this one would never be tired, never be busy, never interested in anything but pleasing me. My dream come true — and the bar was full of them! The city was full of them! A wife who never argued... her English wasn't good enough... The price? Basically, that would depend on the woman's

6

looks, which establishment you are in, and how drunk you are. Prices could be high: if you chose the wrong woman you might get a disease. But don't worry: the Grace Hotel has its own medical clinic. Of course, wallets and watches, gold chains and so forth, have been known to vanish, and it's not easy to run after a thief with your trousers around your ankles.

I decided to pop across the street to the Grace and have a look-see. The Grace Coffee Shop is a notorious pickup spot. If you approach it through the lobby, you are sure to believe you're in Saudi Arabia: this is an Arab hangout and the men are dressed traditionally for Saudis. There are even signs in Arabic. But the girls brought you right back to Thailand. All dressed up with nowhere to go... except upstairs for "exercise," as they called it.

The coffee shop is superficially like any other with its plastic tables and chairs and its loud music from several jukeboxes — the place is big — but of course it is packed with lovely women. All sizes, shapes, ages, and prices. Depending on the woman and the time of day, somewhere between 300 and 500 *baht*. Some even commanded 1,000 *baht* ($40), a dazzling few, even more.

Most of them won't approach you. You have to walk over to them. That is the unwritten rule, though there are occasional exceptions: I saw women literally drag men out of the room to take them to bed. Some of the girls will sit on a man's knee and bounce up and down. After rubbing against him for a while, they might check between his legs to see if they are making the right impression. If he gets lucky he might get a free massage right there at the bar. Some of them pull up their dresses to let men have a quick peek at the merchandise.

I decide to go back to the Bier-Kutsche. After ordering a drink I pick out my woman and smile. She smiles back! I move confidently to the barstool beside her. No sooner have I bought her a drink than a tall German man walks up. She greets him with a radiant smile: he's a friend of hers. Suddenly I am sitting with two drinks before me as they walk out arm-in-arm. Well, who cares... there are 99 more to choose from... Within 30 seconds I am deep in conversation with a new woman. She is older than the first, maybe 40, but well preserved: nice eyes. Pidang is her name. She can speak English quite well. Her name is actually Dang. The "Pi" prefix before her name is a sign of respect for an older person, like "San" in Japanese.

I liked Pidang immediately. We were surrounded by the beautiful young girls I'd heard so much about, and she was a mature woman. But I felt her responsiveness, her warmth and kindness. My fantasies of moving in with a hot young number were rapidly giving way to... friendship. The last thing I'd expected.

Later I discovered that Pidang loved to help people. She was always lending people money... couldn't say no, even when she didn't have much for herself. She was almost fifty, but certainly didn't look it. She'd worked downtown for years but when I met her she'd just come back after being absent for seven. Having worked as a cocktail waitress in Udon Ratchathan and other USAF camps during the Vietnam War, she found herself unemployed once the war was over. Charlie, her next-door neighbor from Bangkok, told her about the money to be made by sleeping with the *farang*. So at 31, off she went to work in Bangkok.

She had long-term relationships with a few men. One was an American who worked in Arabia and came to see her every three months. Eventually he was transferred back to the States. He wrote for a few years, but eventually fell out of the habit.

She had a chance to marry two foreigners and even went so far as to get a passport. One was already married; his wife phoned Pidang. Not wishing to break up a marriage, she bowed out. The other fiance had a friend who fought with Pidang, and her future husband wouldn't stand up for her. One night she threw coffee in his face and tore up her passport.

When she stopped working downtown before, her mother got permission to live and work on a small piece of land for three-fourths of the harvest. The house was on stilts over water in a rice paddy field. Pidang worked in the rice paddies every day, up to her waist in water. Her family at this time included her mother, her father, and a young boy named Lek whom she'd found as a newborn infant at the side of the road in a Mekong Whiskey crate. The umbilical cord was not completely cut at the stomach. Ants were crawling over his face and body. She was unable to make enough money to support them all, so she went back to Bangkok and tried selling food. Her friends finally persuaded her that she was wasting her time and that she'd be better off downtown again. I met her just after her return.

What happened to all the money she made before? She spent it all playing Phi Thong, which is Thai poker. It's illegal, but Thai love to gamble. The element of good luck... *Choke di...*

Between short-times with *farang* she would play upstairs in one of the rooms in the Grace. If she ran out of money all she'd have to do is go down to the coffee shop to make some more.

When she had plenty of money, everybody wanted her. When she had none, nobody did. The usual story. Many of her former friends wouldn't even buy food from her.

Later I found out that she'd spent her first two weeks in town trying to get a man. Her mother came and urged her to give it up and come home since she wasn't having any success. Pidang gave herself another 15 days to try her luck. She cut her hair in an attempt to make herself more attractive, and the night before I met her she did pick up a man, so perhaps the haircut worked. He gave her 500 *baht* and an additional 20 for a taxi. She gave 400 to her mother, then went back to work the next night.

Pidang and I talked untill closing time, about 2:30 am, then walked out together. "Where you hotel?" she asked. "No hotel," I replied. At first she didn't believe me: *farang,* or foreigners, stay in hotels. "Which hotel?"

Eventually she suggested a place, the Playboy Hotel, just around the corner from the Grace.

By then, in the course of discussing a place to stay, we'd walked about a mile. We hailed a *tuk-tuk*, the local three-wheeled motorized form of transportation.

The Playboy Hotel is a short-time place. The rooms are rented to couples for eight-hour periods. At three in the morning we could get the lowest rate: only 140 *bath*. Television was free, but you had to pay extra for a dirty video. Since Pidang was Thai, she did the bargaining with the *tuk-tuk* driver. Thirty *baht* — a little high. Once these drivers saw a woman with a *farang*, the price went up. Still, at three in the morning, who wants to argue about 20 cents, especially when you've got a woman beside you and a hotel ahead?

The bed was round. The walls and ceiling were mirrored. (Mind you, most Thai women want total darkness the first time.) Beside the bed there was a panel for 'lighting mood changes.' There was a round section in the middle of the bed that went up and down when you operated a switch. It made more noise than the Bangkok traffic.

Apparently the up-and-down motion acts as a sexual crutch for the tired, worn-out businessmen who visit Thailand. Anyway, just to see whether I could get away with it, I asked Pidang for 40 *baht* to add to my 100 for the hotel room. She paid up without complaining.

13

The first word of Thai you need to know, after your numbers (you can always use hand signals to arrange a price with a woman) is *"Ab nam!"* — "Take a shower." Thai women are immaculate, and they want you to be clean too. I took my shower first, and Pidang watched me the whole time. She didn't let me watch her when she took hers: Thai women are shy in some unexpected ways.

At noon the phone rang: time to leave the room. We'd anticipated the call and were already dressed for the street. When we emerged, the sun was blinding and the traffic noise deafening. Back to reality.

Somehow, I didn't feel as if I'd spent the night with a prostitute. I've been to bed with my fair share of women: some of them weren't prostitutes, but felt as if they were. Some of them I wished would just go into the bathroom afterwards and flush themselves down the toilet, never to be heard from again. Some I even loved but this was a different feeling.

Pidang and I went to eat once we had left the hotel. Then she persuaded me to take her to see the place where I was staying, a small guest house near the National Library, a long way off. We took a #23 bus. When we got there, I showed her the place from the outside. As with most guest houses, no women were allowed inside — Thai women, that is — so I couldn't bring her in.

It was 1:45 pm, time to say goodbye. She'd never asked me for any money. Having paid the 40 *baht* for the hotel and bought herself a drink the evening before, she had only 40 *baht* left. I decided to give her 100 *baht*. She accepted it silently and I walked away. No sooner had I reached the corner than I changed my mind again, walked back to her, and asked for my money back. She handed it over without a word. I walked away again, returned to her, and gave her 200 *baht*.

Why was I acting so strangely? At the time I didn't understand what was going on in Thailand. I still had some strange Western prejudices against paying a woman to spend the night with me. I didn't find out how little money she had until the day before I left the country. In any case, now that I think about it, so what if I paid her? I've paid every woman in one way or another. I bought them lunch, dinner, a movie, flowers — and more often than not I didn't even get a hug or kiss goodnight or a thank you. If the only reason Pidang was with me at first was

15

money, does it matter? A lot of men and women get married for money in the West. If you can accept a long-term economic contract, why not a short-term one?

A week later, I'd seen Pidang every night. On the seventh day we moved into a "bungalow" on Soi 77 Sukhumvit Road. We'd been in a hotel only once since the Playboy: a small curtain hotel, owned by a Chinese, like most of them. He saw the *farang* coming: 350 *baht* for a room with a cold shower. Lousy room, noisy, a real ripoff. A Thai would probably have paid 100 *baht,* and that would most likely have included a woman. He even asked Pidang for her ID card, the first time in her life that happened, she told me.

A curtain hotel is something like an American motel, except that when you drive up in your taxi a boy pulls a curtain around your vehicle before you get out, so that nobody can see who you are or who you're with. These joints are everywhere. They usually charge between 150 and 300 *baht* (again, about 100 *baht* to Thai). A numbered hotel has no name, just a number, such as Hotel 38. Both numbered and curtain hotels provide a place to make love to your lady, and most supply ladies as well. The ones farther from the tourist areas are the

16

cheapest, of course, although you still pay a higher price than the Thai.

"Bungalow" is the Thai term for any place you live. Our bungalow was a single room, about 18 feet square and about five and a half feet high. By putting my head between the ceiling beams I could stand more or less upright. Outside toilet, outside kitchen, outside shower. In fact, the cooking area and shower were located in the passageway around the house.

We had to buy a bed — 1,500 *baht* — and linoleum for the floor so the mosquitoes, which infest the water under the house, wouldn't come up through the cracks between the floorboards. The sliding wooden window had to be repaired, and a padlock installed on the door. The rent was 500 *baht* a month. The walls between our "bungalow" and the other "bungalows" in this house were made of fiber board, which was so thin you could hear two friends whispering on the other side of it.

Nok, the woman next door — her name means "bird" — lent us a mosquito net. Sort of collateral for the 50 *baht* I'd lent her the week before when she didn't manage to get a man downtown. "This week no sell pussy," she said, and I felt sorry for her.

Nok getting ready to go downtown "to sell pussy."

She told me she was living with her brother and his wife and his baby son Daw. That's because I'm not Thai and wouldn't have understood if she told me she was actually living with a man who was not her husband, their child, and a house girl — sort of a maid — named Boa. They all slept in one room, the same size as ours. She was not married in our sense of the word, not married by the monks — that is, with the blessings of Buddha! Nevertheless, she was living with a man and had a child by him, and in the eyes of some Thai that is a sort of marriage.

The night I met Pidang I asked her to take me home with her, but she couldn't because, like many girls, she was sharing a place. The arrangement was this: She slept all day, then went downtown at night, barhopping until she picked up a man. If she did, she stayed with him in a hotel for the night. If not, she'd stay up all night and, when the Themae closed at 6 am, she'd go sleep all day at her sister's place. Then back to work the next night. The bars she frequented most were the Bier-Kutsche on Soi 3, the Biergarten on Soi 7, the Grace Hotel Coffee Shop on Soi 3, and the Themae Coffee Shop. Because the Themae stays open all night, it's the last-chance bar for the girls.

Not many weeks after we met, Pidang was sitting on the floor of our bungalow, ironing my shirts and jeans. She was wearing her sarong. I've seen a lot of hookers in my life, but she looked much more like a housewife. The paint on the walls must have been a hundred years old and the back wall moved when you touched it. The door didn't close properly. If you didn't close the sliding wooden window on the side of the house when people took a shower outside in the passageway, the water would spray into the room.

One night, Pidang looked depressed. After much questioning she told me she needed 1,000 *baht* so she could officially get Lek, the boy she'd found and taken in, adopted by her mother. I said nothing and let it slide. Two days after that, we were sitting in the Grace Hotel. She was depressed again, all curled up in a ball with her arms wrapped around me. I knew she still didn't have the 1,000 *baht* and I knew the only other way she could earn the money was to go with a *farang.* She obviously didn't relish the thought of going back to work, and she wasn't trying to put one over on me. I realized something was missing from around her neck: she'd pawned her gold chain for the 1,000 *baht.* Well, hell. I gave her 1,100 *baht* to redeem it — 100 *baht* was interest for two days.

Chapter 2

THAI STYLE

It was 6 pm one Saturday and Nok was putting on her makeup. Having cooked supper for her son with the help of her husband, she poked her head in through the doorway to tell Pidang and I she was off to "sell pussy." I gave her some advice on how to wear her hair. She took my advice and hopped a bus downtown. I hoped she would get a man so she could pay me back my 50 *baht*.

The next week, Pidang, Nok and I went downtown together. We all had supper in her sister's house. It was Saturday night, a big night, no work the next day for Mana, who's Jim's husband and Pidang's brother-in-law. Their baby son Daw was there, as were a few friends. Everyone sat cross-legged on the floor. The food was served in dishes on the floor and we each got a plate of rice with a spoon. You could use your hands to eat if you wanted to. Pidang said it tasted better that way. A real family occasion, lots of conversation, lots of laughter. Even though I didn't speak Thai, they wanted to make me feel at home.

There was a hole in the floor. Actually, there were many holes in the floor, but this one was a special hole. People spit down it, put unwanted food in it . . . everything you can imagine. A sort of improvised garbage disposal. It didn't use water like a Western one though. It was just a hole. There was no running water in the house.

Iced water was the drink at mealtime. A large aluminum bowl was passed around and everybody drank out of the same one. I was a visitor so I got my own glass. After the meal, everyone sat around talking. The women were very modest about their movements in sarongs, the men a bit more careless. Playing with the baby took up a lot of the time and conversation.

When the meal and conversation were over, we went downtown in a non-air-conditioned bus (2 *baht*). We got a #25, known for its high-speed racing drivers. When the driver braked, I managed to knock the whole roll of tickets out of the conductor's hand. He stuffed the lot in his shirt and carried on as if nothing had happened.

No one on the bus seemed to notice. They did, though — the "not noticing" is just Thai-style manners.

Once downtown, I went to the Biergarten. Pidang went off and sat by herself. The first man I met complained about the women: "Look at them smile, they smile for no reason!" He told me he was a German engineer, working on the construction of a cement plant. He'd been in Thailand six months and already he seemed bored with the women, poor guy.

Most of the men I talked to had been divorced at least once. It was the second visit to Bangkok for many of them. One man felt cheated. Perhaps he didn't understand about short-term lease agreements, but only long-term marriage ones... The girls might smile for no reason, or perhaps they smiled at the prospect of earning 500 *baht* for an hour's work instead of 70 *baht* for a day hauling cement on a building site in 90-degree weather. That's a little over two dollars a day but for most of them, that was the only alternative.

A Frenchman complained that the girls didn't show their true feelings. I wished he'd been at the Grace Hotel a few nights before, when the woman in the red dress began to scream at a man from Bangladesh, half in English, half in Thai, "Go back home, you asshole! No self-respecting Thai woman will go to bed with you. Go do it with your family!" She spat furiously on the ground. Interesting to see a ravishing woman with long black hair screaming for no apparent reason. Her true feelings? Who knows?

At the other end of Thai society from the hookers were the 'good' girls, who do not sleep with their prospective marriage partners until after the ceremony. Needless to say, there are plenty of available women to relieve the Thai man's sexual frustration. But if his wife or girl friend finds out, he'll probably be slapped around a bit, and he might even lose his fiancee. Thai women do seem to knock their men around a lot. "SALOP SALOP SALI!" is what the Thai say for slapping someone around the face.

Some of the girls who work downtown are honest and some are not. Not all of them are content to make their living by going to bed with men. Some drop drugs in a man's drink before taking him to bed. When he wakes up several hours later he will find out that he has lost his wallet and any other valuables he was foolish enough to have on him. One woman had collected three bungalows, two cars, and a lot of money by operating this way, Nok told me. Of course, if a woman gets caught at this kind of thing she goes to jail, but more often than not she will go free. Since the average tourist's stay is only five days, the woman has only to stay away from work till her victim goes home.

If a man comes to Bangkok and "goes butterfly" — hops from woman to woman in the same bar — some girls will not go with him because they're afraid of being infected by the AIDS virus. Be aware that these girls have spent their lives in bars picking up *farang*, and know just about everything that goes on in the bar. Of course some women do "work butterfly," that is, change men every night, sometimes taking on as many as three in a day. Short-time artists.

Others go in for long-term relationships: a week, a month, or even lengthier arrangements. Anything's possible as long as the cash holds out.

Nok didn't get a man, and so went home. The rent was due and the pressure was on.

Pidang was lying on the bed when I got home. She told me I'd better give her some money, otherwise she'd have to go downtown to work. I'd grown to like her even though I'd only known her a short time. I didn't want to see her go back downtown...

We didn't need a radio or TV. The walls were so thin we could listen to everyone else in the building. As I looked around, I saw our clothes on hangers, hung on nails in the wall — her shoes were by the door. I thought maybe the garbageman would take them away, they were so old and battered.

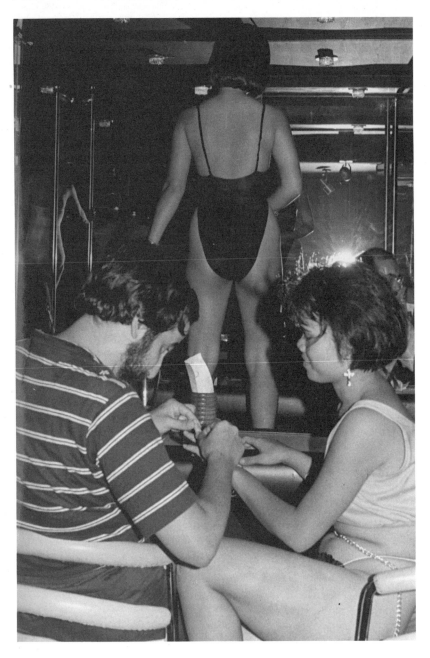

Many Farang fall in love with these charming Thai ladies. But not many of these relationships last. Here the ring goes on the finger.

Taking a shower was simple: you'd stand outside the door and pour water over yourself from a small plastic basin. The water came from large water jars, which were filled up every day from a garden hose. Of course, you'd wear your sarong while you shower. Nudity was forbidden by royal decree. If someone did see your private parts, they'd have *choke mi di* - bad luck. The women were experts at taking showers and changing their clothes behind a curtain improvised from a sarong, exposing only their ankles and shoulders. By the way, you never take a sarong off over your head. Or touch anyone's head in Thailand. The head is considered a temple. Also, don't hang your sarong on a clothesline at the height of your head — *Mi di* — no good.

One day Pidang showed off her cooking. Squid stuffed with pork, hot. Next dish: Potatoes, chicken, and tomatoes cooked in a broth. And whole fish fried in a wok. All with rice. Delicious food! Next day more goodies.

She was generous, too. When she cooked for me there was always enough to give some away to anyone who might come by who didn't have enough food.

She gave sound advice to anyone who asked for it and many people came by to ask her opinion. She never *phut ma* — talked too much.

Our other next-door neighbor" room was twice as big as ours. Four adults and two children were in there. Nok, Boa and Nok's husband Won, with baby Daw, lived on the other side and Pidang and I in our room. We all shared the same toilet.

Ut, another woman who worked downtown, came by one night after supper. She was an old friend of Pidang and Nok, and lived upstairs in the bungalow next door.

Every morning the children would go off to school at 7:30 am. They were spotless, and beautifully turned out. The ones who knew me smiled when they saw me. You'd never guess they came from a slum area, or squatters' houses. The houses and their inhabitants were actually quite clean. It's just that everybody threw garbage out the door. I had a hard time keeping clean under these conditions, but it was no problem for them.

By 8:30 am the men had gone to their work, if they had any, and the women were out washing clothes by hand. Most of the activities connected with water took place on the duckboards around the house. The house was actually on piles sunk into a marsh, and so there was water under the boards. If you dropped a bar of soap while taking a shower, you could kiss

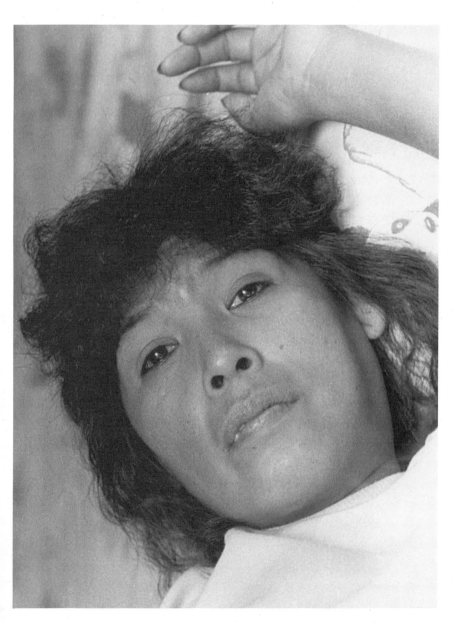

Ut, one of Pidang's friends from the old days.

it goodbye... One day the toilet was occupied, so Nok pulled up her sarong and took a piss right there in the passageway outside the door. The smell of rotting garbage got bad sometimes, and brushing your teeth while looking at rotting food could turn your stomach. Once you could wash, shave, take a shower and brush your teeth without hacking and coughing, you were well on your way to being Thai.

After the housecleaning, laundering and feeding their babies, the women sat around and gossiped. But always in a low voice. Remember, it was very easy to hear through those walls.

Thai women don't do much moaning or express their sexual pleasure verbally. If they did, the whole neighborhood would know when they had sex. Even taking a shower at odd times is a giveaway.

Chapter 3

SOI 77

By January 6, I'd been here in Soi 77 for one week. Pidang didn't go downtown any more. Actually, she wouldn't be working in any case at the moment because she was having her period. Five days a month of enforced idleness — 25 days to hustle. I knew she was having her period because there were blood spots all over the floor and her sarong was wet with blood in the back. She looked embarrassed when I mentioned it to her. Sanitary napkins were a new product here and still very expensive. I gave her money to buy some.

When I went downtown during the day, in both the Bier-Kutsche and the Biergarten I noticed German men holding Thai-looking babies, with Thai girls in tow. Some of the "good men" the Thai girls talk about were now living in Germany and back to see the family for old times' sake.

For all the outside appearance of disorder, there was in fact an amazing amount of discipline in Thai culture, if only in the home. The children, especially the boys, were spanked for misbehavior.

I once heard Jim, the lady next door, spank one of her boys 27 times for misbehavior. Both parents punished the children. On the other hand, love was bestowed with equal lavishness. Babies got a lot of fondling and were carried everywhere. Children are everybody's concern: I was even told that if I saw a child misbehaving I should feel free to spank him myself. I was free to hug him too, they said...

There's not much violence in Thailand. What little there is tends to take place after drinking large quantities of Mekong whisky — a very popular drink, about half as strong as Western whisky. The most common opening move is a soda bottle to the head. This is frequently followed by Thai boxing between the two opponents. Everyone stands back and lets the two opponents work out.

Ut got drunk again last night. She tended to spend her earnings on whisky. Her husband worked for the post office and by Thai standards actually made good money. She was wandering around naked for a while until he ushered her off to bed.

Ut's name actually means "pig" — it's what the Thai call a joke name. They all seem to have one. Ut's refers to her canine teeth, which protrude between her lips. One day someone starts calling you a joke name and it's yours for life.

I went to see the Grand Palace and Wat Po, like any tourist. So many people are stunned by the wealth of the Palace. They'd be even more amazed if they knew something about the way the average Thai lives.

Anyway, I needed to take a piss and one of the few public toilets in all of Bangkok is located on a corner near the Wat. While I was having my piss, two young chaps started peeping and giggling together. I couldn't for the life of me think why. Then I remembered that Thai men aren't circumcised.

When I got home little Daw was loudly calling a woman *he-yai* — "big pussy." I expected him to get smacked, but nobody seemed to care, or even to notice. The woman was one of the few really fat Thai I'd seen.

Nok paid me back the money she owed me — she finally got a man last night. She was also expecting her boy friend from Germany today. "Good," she commented. "Big money." Nice to know what you want from a relationship.

By the way, not all the girls take advantage of their men. One young man told me he'd been going around with a Thai woman for a week when she asked him to take her shopping. He was nervous about the bill she might run up, but all she bought was a toothbrush, soap and shampoo.

There were a lot of big turtles living in the water under our house. They liked bananas. While we were feeding them a woman came by selling lottery tickets. I bought number 13, which she told me was a lucky number. They cost 20 *baht* each — a lot of money for Thailand. The lottery in Thailand is a big public occasion. Everyone buys a ticket. One of the most popular songs alludes to it: *"Oh Buddha / I give you silver, I give you gold / Buddha, I give you chickens and ducks / Give me the winning lottery number."* In the end, Buddha sells all his gold and chickens to buy lottery tickets, but he doesn't win the lottery. Nobody wins the lottery. The group who made the record is called Calabow; the name of the record is *Welcome to Thailand.* Even monks buy tickets.

There was a practical alternative to the lottery: where I lived there was an institution called the money pool. Members put in 10 *baht* a day every day for a month. You could borrow twice from the pool, but it had to be 150 *baht* each time and if you borrowed once you had to borrow the second time. If on a particular day you wished to borrow money, you'd go to a meeting of the women who are paying into the pool and want to borrow from it. You'd take part in a secret bidding. One woman might bid

34

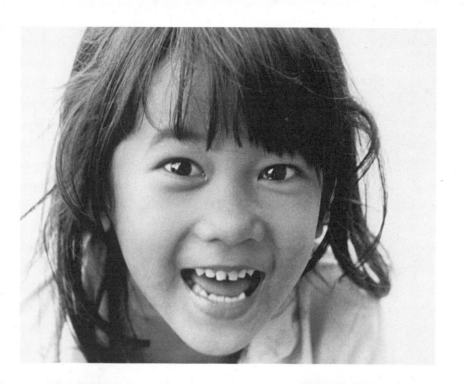

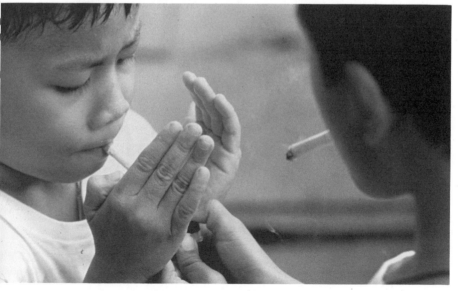

Top: The happiest girl in my neighborhood.
Bottom: Boys will be boys.

35

5 *baht*, another 6 *baht*, and so on. The one with the highest bid wins the 150-*baht* loan. But she'd have to pay the amount of her bid in addition to her regular daily payment until the end of the month, and of course she's required to borrow twice. In the end, those members of the pool who haven't borrowed split the remaining money equally. The young woman who runs the system puts in 10 *baht* a day. Since she never has to borrow, she's in on the split at the end of the month. There are also 30-*baht* and 50-*baht* pools. Pidang and I joined the pooling system, figuring we couldn't lose.

While I was taking a shower tonight Jim, next door, decided that as usual everybody should know where I was and what I was doing. *"Rory ab nam!"* she shouted. "Is he naked?" shouted someone else. The Thai do have a good sense of humor.

One night when Pidang and I went to her sister's house for supper, Jim, Pidang's sister, was crying her eyes out. Mana, her husband, was yelling at her. He called her a lazy buffalo. She went into the bedroom and put on makeup, then came out and sat cross-legged with Dong's body between her knees — he fit perfectly. This high-energy evening turned into a competition, starring me. All the young men in the neighbor-

Chi, my next door neighbour, showing off his knowledge
of western sign language while brushing his teeth in the
shower.

hood came around to see if they could push me over while I sat cross-legged. Nobody made it. The men accepted me more after that. We all decided we'd go running tomorrow morning. Another trial for the *farang*... The Thai as a race have never been conquered.

The men were outside my door at 5:30 this morning, dressed for the run. It was about three miles. We passed through the rich district about a mile and a half from where we live: a sort of walled compound with a barrier and guards at the entrance. The houses were magnificent by any standards. Fountains in the front garden, four cars in each garage, arches, columns, — the works. The guard at the entrance nearly dropped dead when he saw me running with four Thai boys. In fact it was so hot and humid I'd taken my shirt off, and he shouted something in Thai about putting it back on before I ran in the compound. I pretended not to understand him and shouted *Lawn* — Hot! He nodded and smiled.

No cats or dogs running around (my neighborhood's full of them). Probably no rats, either... all this only a mile and a half from home. The compound has its own water tower. The streets were clean, no garbage lying around. No noisy smoke-belching buses. Another world!

It was a good run. One of the men, Git, got blisters on his feet because he had no socks. I gave him a pair of mine when we got home. After the run we went to an outdoor restaurant and had hot sweet milk with a raw egg mixed in it, and Thai-style croissants. Mana apologized for the incident last night. I thought it must be for hitting his wife in front of me, but later I found out it was because she'd misbehaved in front of me! When we went back to his house after the run, she was still in bed so he screamed at her to get up. She did, started crying again, and blew her nose on the dress she was wearing, the same one as last night. She'd slept in it.

It was three weeks since I moved into Soi 77. People were starting to recognize me. Even some of the women smiled at me — polite but distant.

Like many women Pidang worked downtown to help support her family. Her father-in-law came by one day and she gave him 1000 *baht.* Later I remarked that we couldn't afford to buy food now that she'd given away all that money. She was hurt by my comment, and even though her sister bought food with the 50 *baht* I gave her, and cooked it, Pidang is refusing to eat. Jim said she'd seen Pidang crying. I tried to persuade Pidang to cheer up and have something to eat, but she refused. She put on her warpaint and said she was going downtown to find a man and make some money. (What an artist she is with makeup! She can make herself look 20 years younger.) Eventually she decided not to go... took off her makeup and made me some tea. This was a proud lady, independent and strong — but gentle too.

To make up for insulting her, I cleaned up the bungalow. I emptied the ashtray over the galvanized tin fence that separates the duckboards and shower from the garbage heap on the other side. The rats were running around as usual. Luckily, they're afraid of humans.

The dogs in the neighborhood were split up into two groups. Every so often there would be a barking or snarling competition between the rival gangs.

They'd fight over food from the garbage pile, territory, or bitches. The bitches took sides with their favorite dogs, reminding me of husbands and wives.

The neighbor in the house next door would get drunk every so often. The first thing he would do is fight with his wife. He started yelling and screaming, breaking things and slapping her around. Pidang and I were sitting in the doorway at 2 am when Charlie, who also lives in the house next door, came back from dancing. I asked him what was going on. He has a Thai mother and a German father, so his English is good. "Not my business," he replied: a standard Thai comment. If it's a family fight and it's not your family, it's not your business. That's Thai style. The night watchman knew that too: just banged his gong twice — 2 am and all's well — and went on his way.

Horn and bell sounds in the street all day. The first sound in the morning was the converted bugle of the coffee vendor — three *baht* for a cup of coffee. "Cafe lawn." (Downtown at the Ambassador Hotel it costs 60 *baht*!) Once you know the sound of each vendor's bell or horn, you know who's out there without looking: the coffee man, the ice cream man, the man who pedals by with something sweet.

Top: Dong gets teeth brushing lessons.
Bottom: Outside my bungalow. On the right is the charcoal burning cooker with a saucepan on top for cooking rice. The cats are in the "shower." This is also the passageway around the house.

42

What sort of people taught English to the Thai in this neighborhood? They all say, *"Hey, you!"* I was slowly teaching them, one by one, to say, "Hello, Rory." Politely. I explained that *"Hey, you!"* is what you say to a *ma* — a dog. Thai are by nature polite, but they think "Hey, you!" *is* polite...

The charcoal lady came around every day. Most people use charcoal to cook. Only people with lots of money have gas rings — almost nobody around here.

I'd been giving English lessons to some adults and children. The Thai language is tonal. That is, the same word can be pronounced with a rising, falling, high, low or level tone and can have several meanings depending on the tone. For instance, the woman who runs the outdoor restaurant on the vacant lot nearby is named Moy. I'd greet her like this: *"Sawatdee khap Moy!"* (Women say, *"Sawatadee ka."*) But everyone would laugh when I said it. After a while I found out I'd been saying, "Good evening, Pubic Hair." The Thai have a sense of humor... Even if it hadn't amused them, most likely they'd have said, *Me be li:* "Never mind." Thai are tolerant of Farang errors.

These school girls came by my bungalow from time to time for help with their English home work and to get to know their first farang. What beautiful intelligent children.

Pidang seemed happier those days. She was learning not to give money away. She's a generous woman, even when it's her money. Thai are naturally generous. For example, if we were eating a meal and Nok walked past the door, Pidang casually invited her to eat with us: *Nok kin khao?* "Nok eat rice?" If I'd go by a bungalow where they were eating, I'd get the same treatment. No need to starve in Thailand. Pidang told me it's common courtesy to give the invitation. The reply, if the passerby doesn't want to eat, is *Kin khao laow* — I've already eaten — *khop kaoon khrap* — Thank you (for a man) or *khop kaoon ka* (for a woman).

Every evening the women, and sometimes the men, would gather around the garbage pile to talk while it burned. It was more comfortable out there: the rooms are too small to hold many people. Besides, it wasn't the rainy season and it was often cooler outside at night than inside. There was a lot of communal hanging out in this area.

Ban comes around every so often to our bungalow to "borrow" food or money. She lives close by in what can only be described as a pile of garbage. "No husband" Pindang says. "No one to look after her."

Last night I took a shower with four women — a first-time experience. I'd seen four naked women take a shower on stage in Pat Pong, the spectacular sport district of Bangkok, but now I was actually in the shower with these four. They all wore sarongs. All I got to see was Jim's ankle. Thai women are so modest that they don't even wear shorts in the streets of Bangkok. Only *farang* girls go around half-naked. Most Thai women wore sarongs at home.

Pidang's stepfather and mother live in Prapradaeng, in a house on stilts over water in a rice paddy field. Lek, the boy Pidang found seven years ago by the side of the road in a whisky crate, also lives with them. The 1,000 *baht* I gave her the first week allowed the family to register the child with the police as the son of Pidang's mother. He couldn't be Pidang's son legally because she's not married. She was married years ago, but the man left her. She had a baby back then but he died. I asked Pidang what she was doing picking up babies in the street, with all the problems that involved. Her answer: "What would you do, let him die?"

Pidang told me she needed 1,000 *baht* a month for the next six years to pay for the boy's schooling till he reaches the age of 16. Then he would go to work with Mana at the Caterpillar maintenance facility in Bangkok. There's no state-paid education in Thailand. In fact I got the feeling, after meeting many women downtown, that the *farang* money spent on sex mostly went to educate Thai children so they wouldn't end up like their mothers. (The rest goes to support the women's elderly relatives, especially their mothers.)

This year her brother in law Mana will go to a local wat for three months to be a monk. He was lucky — when he was 21, he drew a black lottery ticket. If he'd drawn a red one, he would have had to do two years in the army in addition to the three months as a monk.

Chapter 4

DAY TO DAY LIVING

One Sunday in January, Pidang and I went on a tour of four wats and a national park. The tour was run by a local man who hires the bus and sells the tour door-to-door.

The cost was only 100 *baht* each. It was a good trip. We stopped at several markets along the way, where the women on the tour who live around Soi 77 bought lots of fresh vegetables and other goodies. *Mi pang* — not expensive, they said. Along the way we stopped at a gas station. I could have been in America, except that the station attendants were Thai. And of course we got to eat a lot of good cheap Thai food at the stalls at the station. The Thai are devout Buddhists. Ninety percent of the people

There are a lot of fairs in the streets of Bangkok every
weekend — and this is a good occasion for the monks
from the local *wats* to come out and sprinkle the people
with water for good luck. Much like a Christian blessing
with Holy Water.

50

practice the religion. A lot of gold leaf was put on the Buddhas we saw, and a lot of candles and incense were burnt, and bells rung for good luck. By the way, don't smell the flowers before you give them to a Buddha. No good. *Mi di.*

Many men would have described Pidang as the perfect wife. She looked well. Always kept my clothes clean. Always glad to see me. Always willing to make love, always attentive to my needs. I tried to do the same for her. "A good girl," everybody tells me. "Good heart!" — high praise in the Thai culture. She was learning home economics from me, showed me the bargains she got in the shops. She began to refuse to buy things at the market if she thought they were too expensive. Before I came, she just bought what she needed no matter what it cost.

When we first moved in, we had to borrow two plates, two forks and two spoons — and one glass — from her sister. Now Pidang has accumulated six glasses, which came free with the detergent she uses. Also two large bowls, two small dishes, some knives, forks and spoons — all at bargain prices. She even bought a money box, with only one opening in it. She raided my pockets for change every evening and put it in her piggy bank.

Nok complained to Pidang that she has to work night and day. In the daytime she looked after the baby, Daw, and at night she had to go downtown to work. Won, her husband, had no job. Of course many Thai men have wives who sell themselves to the male *farang*. Such a wife can earn 500 *baht* a day instead of the 70 to 100 *baht* she might earn from a regular job.

When I got home from downtown today there had been a police raid. They were looking for people playing *Phi Thong* — Thai Poker, which is illegal, and of course for drugs. Well, they found cardplayers but no drugs. "Monkey go to jail" is the expression the Thai use when you get caught doing something illegal, and some monkeys went to jail. Four hundred *baht* to get out. Money will get you out of most problems in Thailand. Mana came home one day for lunch. He'd been stopped in a spot check for pollution. In Bangkok? The fine for excess pollution is 600 *baht*, but 100 *baht* on the spot to the checker solved his problem.

The nice woman who lives next to Jim and Mana got drunk on Mekong whisky this morning and threw all the kids out of the house.

Today is January 28th. A group of us hired a *tuk-tuk* and went off to the Green Lawn Country Club. A golf club with every amenity, built for rich Thai and *farang*. Still under construction.

We sat beside one of the water traps and everybody went swimming. Just like Pattaya, they said. That's the main seaside resort for package tours from Europe. When it cooled off a bit, down to about 88° Fahrenheit, a net was brought out and Pidang, Ut and Nok went into the water to fish for shrimp. They got lots. Then they prepared the shrimp live with hot peppers and hot sauce, and we ate them raw. Delicious. As we were eating, I noticed that the building workers were taking their evening *ab nam* — shower — in the water trap. On most building sites, the workers build a place for themselves to live while they're at a particular site. I guess this was a good job for them: they had a swimming pool beside their tin huts, and fishing as well.

When we got back home, there was a fight in progress between two drunken neighbors.

There's nothing more comical than seeing two drunken Thai attempting to be Thai boxers and rolling around in the dirt. Eventually, one man's sister came out and slapped her brother around, swearing and yelling at him. That ended the fight. If there was a culprit, it was once again that cheap Mekong whisky. Poor people drink whisky. The rich drink beer, which is much more expensive.

I wish they hadn't fought, because Moy, the woman who runs the open-air restaurant on the vacant lot, was so absorbed in the goings-on that she burned my supper.

Pidang was giving food away again. All the bananas I bought were handed out to the children when they came home from school.

On January 30th, I went to a Thai doctor, whose 170 *baht* fee included both the visit and the medication. I thought of all those poor *farang* going to the doctors downtown and paying American prices. Not to mention all the poor Thai who pay two days' wages for a five-minute visit. Doctors are the same in every country: rich.

Boa, the live-in house girl for Nok, is five months pregnant. She's a second wife: the father came by but refused to pay her rent. That's why she works for Nok. She'd been staying with

54

Jim, but moved out. She looks sad and seems worried: no home, no food, no husband. Her only hope is the kindness of her friends.

February 2: at 4:30 am in the morning, a nearby house caught fire and burned to the ground. Everybody came out to watch. It was lucky there was no wind, otherwise the whole area would have gone up. Dry wood burns fast and the fire department took a long time to arrive. People were throwing buckets of water on the blaze, but the flames were 30 feet high. When the fire was finally out, everybody stood around talking about it. The shop opened... people bought sodas and what have you and put on their music.

The police came the next day to investigate, walking about with their batons out. They're not comfortable walking around this area. The old man who owned the bungalow that burned down was taken to hospital with burns on his arms and legs. His family and tenants were now homeless. A government relief agency came by later on to give the people rice and blankets and a little money. I made a small donation myself.

Ut's husband is having a birthday party outside, beside the garbage dump. Even the black and white cat, *"Maeu Loly"* or Rory's Cat, so called because I feed her, is in on the party.

Thai cannot pronounce their R's. *Maeu* always hangs around when Pidang is cooking.

Pidang, Charlie and I don't drink alcohol, so when we refused to drink at the party, the joke was that there were "only three girls at the party: Charlie, Pidang and Rory." Thai joke. But when they finished laughing, they remarked seriously, "Rory good man, no drink whisky."

Boa's husband still hasn't turned up. Today Pidang asked me if I wanted Boa to move in with me. Pidang offered to move out and live with her sister. Since Boa doesn't know the downtown scene, said Pidang, not only is she pregnant and resourceless, she also has to learn the ropes before she can do business. Pidang remarked that she wouldn't mind if I prefer this arrangement, which would help Boa. I knew Pidang was testing me so I told her I'd think about it. She looked sad.

Boa's female friends who lived in the immediate area were having a meeting this morning. They decided that if the baby's father didn't turn up, everyone would chip in to give her her fare home and some spending money. Boa, who already had three children at home, burst into tears. Well, what more can they do for her?

I can't believe it's February 5. Pidang and I went on another tour. We had a good time. The bus carried 50 Thai and me. We were lucky to have an on-board engineer/mechanic: the rear springs broke and we got a flat tire in Pisanulok so we spent the night at Lumsac Koaka Palatan, a *wat* that was still under construction.

As night fell, Pidang and I walked around the half-constructed buildings by the light of the stars. "Aren't they beautiful?" I asked. "Yes, but no have stars in Bangkok," she replied.

We got up at 6:30 am to go and see the sunrise at Kow Caw, where the king's new summer residence and country retreat is under construction. At a nearby war museum, we were shown a video of the war 14 years ago between Thailand and Laos, and received a briefing about the Communist threat in the area. There were only a few army personnel about and the ones at the king's residence had unloaded guns. The museum had cases of captured Russian-made arms, photos of Marx and Lenin and a Communist flag. The briefing officer told us of a battle in which he lost three friends.

When we got back from our tour, Ut was drunk and fighting with Nit's mother Boon. The aggravations had been going on for some time, so Ut and her husband Theo decided to move. Meanwhile, they parked all their belongings in our tiny room. One rabbit, five large cardboard cartons, one plastic garbage can used as a suit-case, two shelves, two stools and a fan. Luckily I was going to Penang, Malaysia for a couple of weeks to renew my visa.

Pidang managed to spend 1,100 *baht* while I was away. "Chinese New Year," she said. "Had to buy chickens and ducks." I reminded her that she's only half-Chinese, and therefore should have bought only half a chicken and half a duck. It's only once a year, she protested.

Taking a shower was exciting today. The wooden boards broke under my feet, plunging me knee-deep in dirty water. At least I managed not to drop the soap. When the neighbors passed by, the men tugged at my sarong to see if they could pull it off. Some even tapped me on the behind. Only the men, though, and Pidang says it's OK between men — a sign of friendli-ness.

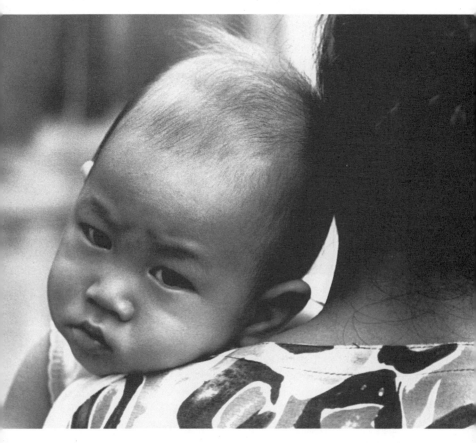

Burt "my baby". I was made an honorary father. Burt and I became so intimate that he felt free enough to piss all over my bed. *"Choke Di"* said Pidang. "Good luck." Burt was trained to stretch out his arms every time anybody called my name.

Da, who worked downtown for years and is now married and living nearby, brought her baby Burt to see me every day. She put him in my arms. He was five months old. At first he was frightened by the stranger's face, but he's gotten used to me and when he sees me he shows that he wants to be in my arms. He pissed all over me today. *"Choke di,"* said Da sympathetically: "Good luck."

Suddenly everybody was outside, shouting, *Chang!* "Elephant!" Three men on an elephant have shown up to sell ivory jewelry to the neighborhood.

When I got back to the bungalow I found a man (from the look of him half-Thai and half-black) on my bed. Who was he?

Pidang explained: When she was working the NCO club, she had a house girl. One day while Pidang was out shopping, a friend of hers came by with her baby boy and asked the house girl to look after him for a while. She never returned. Pidang couldn't take care of the baby, so she gave him to some people she knew. His name is King and he was now 18 and planning to join the army. He thinks Pidang is his real mother and she hadn't told him the truth yet. Of course what Pidang tells me may not be the truth, but somehow I believe her. I've never caught her in a lie.

King stayed with Pidang's sister for a few days. I noticed he had no socks, so I gave him a pair. He was very grateful. He told me he wanted to go to America to find his dad. I tried to steer him away from that plan. To be poor in Thailand, I explain, is one thing, but to be poor, half Black and half Thai in America is quite a different matter.

For a long time, every night Nok, Ut, Pidang and I made plans to go downtown, but we never got around to going. Eventually Pidang and I went by ourselves. She got sick so we had to come back early. However, it was worth the trip: we got involved in a #25 bus race down Sukumvit Road, a thrill a minute. Sixty miles an hour at least, and we won!

When we got home, Ut was drunk again. Her husband had gone off to a *lomen cha* — a Chinese teashop, really a massage parlor — with three of his friends. "Theo good man," she says. "Friends bad men!" A good man in Thailand is one who works for his wife and her family. "Thai men no go work no pussy," she added. "My husband give me enough money, but I spend it on whisky." Charlie, who was in on this conversation, added: A Thai man must buy lots of things for his wife, so he'd better work. If he does, he gets pussy. if not, she goes somewhere else and finds a new man — Thai style!

Nok was drunk tonight too. She had no money and her husband had been gone for two days. (When he did come home the next day, he told us he had been in jail for playing poker. Eight-hundred-*baht* fine. His father bailed him out.)

Today was lottery day. Everybody who was at home or near a radio was listening to the lucky numbers. By about 4:30 pm in the afternoon, the young boys were in the street selling the lucky number list for one *baht*. Everybody seemed to have a number close to the winning one, and a good excuse for not having precisely the winning one. Pidang remembered a number on the receipt we got from a man who asked for money for the families of the dead. The last two numbers were the same as the last two of the winning number — except reversed. Close but no cigar.

I offered to take Nok, Ut and Dong downtown one night and buy them all a few drinks. Even to pay for an air-conditioned bus. They all refused. The word about AIDS is out. Theo, Ut's husband, didn't want her going downtown any more. Nok was nervous too. I explained to Theo that Ut would just be going out for a drink, not to work, and he said he understood.

62

Nok was 42. Her English was quite good. She'd been working the international circuit: Germany for eight months, Singapore... She'd also worked Hong Kong businessmen's parties. She talked a lot about going back there, because the money was so good. After working 13 years, she was still basically broke. Most of the money went for alcohol and male Thai dancers. These chaps — very good-looking men, by the way — are worshipped by the women who support them. A good thing, because they're not paid much. When a man dances, the women press around the edge of the stage and make donations, asking for dates after the show. Often they get into relationships this way. Then they support him, buy him presents, jewelry, take him out, pamper him... But, just like the girls, these men take off when a lover's money runs out.

Nok made good money in Germany. An agent came to town, got her a visa, and arranged all the necessary papers. The split was 50-50. But she had a fight with him so she hit him with a bottle and came home.

Won, Nok's husband, got a job as a gravedigger, but money was still short — Chinese gravediggers don't make much, so the situation continued to deteriorate next door.

In contrast, Pidang was becoming very affectionate — she often put her arms around me, and she cooked me beautiful meals. Cuddled up to me in bed. But I could see the suspicion in her eyes when I'd come home from downtown.

What a woman — a true friend. She didn't say much, her actions spoke for themselves. You could feel what was going on in Thailand if you became sensitive to the people. Their faces might look expressionless sometimes, but that's because it's rude to show your feelings in public. The feelings were there. At home, of course, people expressed themselves more freely, but there was still a subtle Thai way of doing it.

Thai society is very strict. They don't think it's right to marry a *farang*. In fact, any woman walking down the street with one is considered a prostitute. If a Thai woman who's married to a Thai man goes downtown to work, it's not the woman who's bad but her husband, who lives on the money she earns. "Bad husband, doesn't work for his wife." If the woman marries another man, that's no problem. He doesn't think of her as a bad girl for going with *farang* before they were married. But if a Thai woman marries a *farang*, even if she works in a bank and has met him there, the marriage is unacceptable. No mixed marriages. If she divorces the *farang*, no one thinks badly of her: she was temporarily under *farang* influence.

One morning I came home from a night out with a woman named Dang, to discover Pidang with a new hairdo, looking about 28. She informed me she was going downtown to work that evening. "You go short-time!" she yelled. I hadn't, and explained at length, but it was no use. Her mind was made up.

Things were at the yelling stage between Nok and Won, too. She'd decided she wanted to leave him. Money is the problem, so Nok asked me to write a letter to her Swiss boyfriend to get him to send her money. She was determined not to work any more, but she had no other way to live.

About 12:30 am the same night, a drunken man walked in through the front door of our bungalow and sat down weeping. His wife had left him to marry a *farang*. He had three children to look after. He didn't blame her, he said, continually shaking my hand. He was just broken-hearted and needed someone to talk to.

March 10. I told Pidang a coalition of women's groups had protested at the airport against sex tours of Thailand. She asked whether the protesters had volunteered to pay for food, education and health care for the families of the girls who work downtown.

If the girls were to go on strike, the Thai balance of payments would be in bad shape. Let's face it, most of the two million men who go to Thailand will spend a minimum of 500 *baht* on one girl.

I spent another night out. When I came home, Pidang was furious. "You go butterfly!" She didn't speak to me all morning and wouldn't look me in the face. She didn't wash my clothes today, and has not gone *bi talad* — to the market. Gone on strike, I guess. She looked unhappy and that made me sad.

When she finally did speak, it was to say she's going downtown tonight — *Bi thio* — literally, "go for a wander." On the way to our bungalow, I passed some neighbor women and they screamed "Butterfly!" at me The men wanted to know, *"Senuk mah?"* — did I have a good time? I had to smile: I'd really become a part of people's

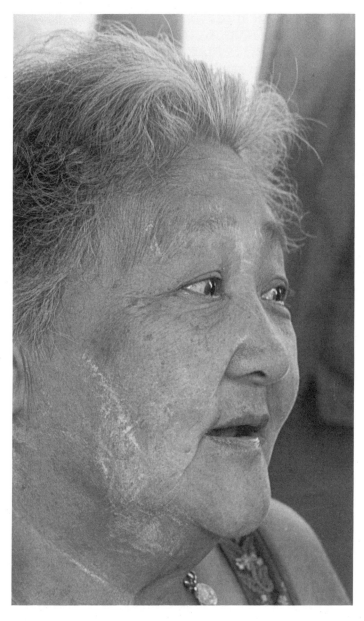

Pidang "good girl" was the limit of this neighbours
English.

lives here. All in all, everyone seemed glad to see me. They were worried. When I told them I was on Soi 22, *"Soi yee sip sawng,"* they tell me I'm lucky to be alive. One man wants to know if I got *"smoking"* — you can figure out what he means if you know where you put a cigar.

When Pidang and I were finally on speaking terms, she told me I had been lucky. "Watch out for the drugged cigarettes," she said. "When you're high you can lose all you own — or worse. When they call your name you don't come — only your name remains."

Pidang and I fought it out. She said she was leaving me — got as far as packing all her stuff in a large brown paper bag. Thai are very physical in private: she slapped me across the face, I spanked her behind a few times, and she decides to stay for a while longer.

At one point I was pulling her out the door by her feet. *Ab nam,* I said, "shower." She couldn't stop laughing.

The day before, she'd been standing outside the door, preparing to take a shower, when I came up with a full bucket and poured it over her head. *"Ahhea!"* she screamed. (The most common Thai curse-word. It's like *merde* in French, or "shit" in English, but a bit stronger.)

The police raided a nearby house again, looking for cardplayers. Chi, the boy next door, escaped by running away.

After our fight, Pidang cooked squid stuffed with pork. Very hot, so hot she had to wash her mouth out. I proudly refrained from washing mine: hot Thai food is unbelievably hot.

Thai have a high tolerance for noise — they have no choice. The traffic in Bangkok has to be heard to be believed. When a red light creates relative quiet, all you hear is the blaring of pop music from one of the bootleg tape vendors' stands.

On Soi 77 the TV sets blare all day. And so do the radios. Jim, next door, swore constantly at her children, or at her husband, in a high-pitched scream. I developed the ability to sleep right through the day, just as the Thai do: *Bi nawn* — go to sleep.

Daw just loved to piss out the door of his bungalow.
Lucky somebody's sandals were not in his favorite spot.

The next time I went to Soi Cowboy, about ten Special Forces Americans, based in Okinawa, were marching in and out of the bars. They were twice the size of most of the girls. It reminded me of the R&R days of the Vietnam era. I sat outside the Old China Hand and Miles, a 55 year old American, came by and sat down beside me. He'd married a Thai woman, an admiral's daughter, whom he met at a party thrown by a big U.S. corporation to try and sell computers to the Thai Navy. He's the marketing director for Southeast Asia. He didn't go with the women any longer. Having told me that, he proceeded to put his arm around a young lady named Oy and vanished.

On my way home, down Soi 77, I met Pidang going downtown to look for me. She was afraid something might have happened to me, she said, but I believe she thought I had another woman. What the bloody hell had happened to her? She'd gotten so jealous and possessive, I honestly think if she'd found me with a woman she'd have killed both of us.

March 26. Ut came by this morning. She looked much better since she stopped going downtown and moved into her new apartment.

The other night there was supposed to be Thai dancing and the next day a movie at the

wat. This always happened when someone died, but the police prohibited the dancing. They allowed it last time, but only because some members of the dead woman's family were in the Army and the Army had authority over the police.

Nok and Ut were selling food at the *wat* and in the vacant lot in front of the house. They hadn't been downtown in a long time — too scared about AIDS. It was not unusual for the girls who work the bars to stop for a while and take up selling food. Usually, the lure of good money brought them back to work, but Nok and Ut were determined not to go back.

Every evening, one of us — Nok, Jim, Dang or I — filled up the water jars outside the door with a garden hose. The water was used for everything except drinking. It was non-potable.

Once the water jars were filled, Si, the older woman next door, took *ab nam*. She stripped to the waist and took the shower half-naked. She was the only woman who did so. The younger women were very careful not to expose their bodies. She spent most of the day walking about, talking rubbish to herself. *"Ba,"* says Nok: "mad."

Daw, Nok's son. Munches corn on the cob. His mother was selling them at the *wat* to avoid going downtown to pick up men.

Today I woke up to the sound of shattering glass. Jim, next door, had thrown a bottle of Mekong whisky out the door of her bungalow. Next she threw out her husband Lung. We all thought he'd been working long hours, but actually he'd been out with a woman from his workplace. He's now refused to give Jim the money for the children's schooling. She collected all his belongings — his tapes, his records, his favorite cowboy boots — and threw them on the garbage heap. Pidang and Si retrived them and hid them in our bungalow. Si just walked by the door with the remains of Lung's shirt, which Jim had ripped up.

It must be almost full moon, because when I got home the other night at about 11, Boon, Nit's mother, was drunk. Her husband was drunk and they were fighting and screaming and breaking things in the bungalow next door to ours. I could hear him punching her, and hear the kids begging him to leave her alone, but the rule in Thailand is "Not my business," and I was becoming a Thai.

Boon didn't appear for a few days. When she did, she had bruises around her eyes. Her husband, who drives his own bus, didn't go to work for three days. Quite a loss for him, of course. Nobody made any comments to either of them. Life goes on.

Tonight we went to Wat Ma Habut, the local *wat*. There was a movie, because some local men are becoming monks. Da, the neighbor who used to work downtown — in fact, she even worked in Germany — was there with her husband, selling pork sausage. She hasn't worked for a few years now. I bought two of her sausages, but couldn't eat them because the taste was too strong. The skins are made of real pig's intestines. It's not that I'm squeamish, but hey, they really taste strong — even Pidang couldn't eat them.

Ut was there with Nok, selling corn on the cob. I wondered how many other women who'd worked downtown were selling food at the *wat*. The corn was boiled in salt water, then covered with a sauce of melted butter and grated coconut. Delicious.

Pidang and I also bought some fried banana fritters, made of bananas and grated coconut and sugar. The movie was about a man who raped and killed a woman while he was drunk.

She came back to haunt him. Eventually he was driven to suicide. As usual in Thai movies, the women have a magic aura about them — and they always dominate the men.

The following morning, Pidang and I smelled something bad in the room. A mouse had crawled in behind the mattress on the floor and died. I was "volunteered" to clean up the mess. Afterward, I decided to have a shower. Picked up a sarong and splash! — all the tea in the new teapot Pidang had bought me went all over the place. I'd been telling her a few days earlier about tea cosies, and how in Ireland we used them to keep the teapots warm. Nobody can fault her for not listening — but a sarong tea cosy!

It was the hot season in Bangkok. Not only hot, but humid. Pidang bought a fan. She finally broke down and went into my wallet for the first time: took 500 *baht.*

In the garage opposite, the green Rolls Royce was back again. They'd managed to fix the other three Rolls, but the green one kept on coming back. I felt sorry for the owner, who never got to drive it. Another day one of the mechanics started up one of the other Rolls to move it out of the way. It jumped into gear and bashed into another Rolls. It's a hard life being rich.

I had seen more Rolls while living on Soi 77 than I'd ever seen in my life. And more Mercedes as well.

Thailand was indeed the Land of Smiles, the Land of Never Mind. However, I saw a man one morning who had been caught stealing on Sukhumit Road. He was kicked and pushed by everyone who had anything to do with the incident. It was certainly merciless. The police passed by on a motorbike. They saw nothing and nobody called them. If you fight one Thai, you fight them all.

Pidang's father came by to pick up the 1,000 *baht* a month I've been giving her to help them out. He took the money and got away as fast as he could.

When I came back from an outing to the Lomen Chas and curtain hotels, Pidang checked my wallet to see how much money I spent, and

The pit crew. These young men repair Rolls Royces in the
repair shop across the street.

whether the condom I kept there was gone. She interrogated me without mercy. When she found no condom, I had no time to explain. She slapped me hard on my naked back. "Go fuck downtown all day and all night!" she said. "That you job!" There was a wrestling match for the wallet. I let her have it. She told me if I went butterfly again she'd leave me. Apparently selling pussy downtown is one thing; buying pussy downtown is quite a different matter. (She was right, too, I *had* been with a woman. The giveaway was that when I got home I took a shower straightaway. You live and learn.)

A friend of Nok's came by to stay with her for a day or two while she waited for money. She was going to marry a Saudi she met in the Grace Hotel. Not exactly a pleasant prospect: they were going to live in Saudi Arabia, and the status of women in that country is well known. Pidang said it was simple: the woman wanted money, and no doubt her future husband had some. I didn't know if she was going to be a bonded woman or not. A lot of the women were sold by their parents to rich Saudis for three to five years.

Daw, Nok's son, just pissed out the door again. His favorite trick. Unfortunately it attracts flies — *man wan* — which of course we had plenty of, since we all threw our garbage over the galvanized-tin fence around the house, or even just out the door. It was an easy habit to pick up.

One of the nice things about living in a Thai community was that there were lots of children, all ages. People always passing by the door. A feeling of community spirit, yet everyone's privacy was respected. We lived on top of each other. If someone sneezed next door, it might as well be in the same room. Babies screamed, women yelled, men grunted, TVs blared, and stereos blasted out. But somehow the noise was not that disturbing; you got used to it, you became part of the family.

If you needed something from the shops, but were feeling too lazy to go — laziness is not a bad thing in Thailand, just a state of being — you could always ask one of the children to go for

Watch Out! *Shongan* — Thai New Year is an occasion for fun and games, especially water-throwing. All for good luck. This is the action at Prapradang, a town on the outskirts of Bangkok. The celebrations are so widely known that this is a nationally televised event.

you. Why not? It would cost you one *baht* and you'd get service with a smile.

By now, the hot season was there, and so was the Thai New Year — April 13. Downtown was deserted. Most of the girls had gone home to be with their families. Of course, *nit noy* — a few — were still out there working. There are workaholics in every field of endeavor.

Shongan — Thai New Year lasts a whole week. The Thai go mad. They throw water at each other. They smear liquid talcum powder on each other's faces and wherever else they can — all for good luck.

Sanam Luong, a large park opposite the National Museum, was a good spot to watch the action. (By the way, on a normal day you could find yourself some female company here. Not during the New Year madness, though.)

At Prapradaeng, groups of youths drove around in pickup trucks and threw water over everything and everybody.

Thai normally don't touch in public — even boy friends and girl friends don't hold hands in the street — but for a week everybody joined in the fun. They even touched each other's heads, which was otherwise a very strong taboo in Thailand.

If you didn't bring any water, you could buy an ice-cold bag of it for about one *baht*. John Hobson, a bald English photographer I knew, was a favorite target — Thai men generally aren't bald — but of course all *farang* are targets. They pretty much left Pidang alone: she was regarded as an older women and the Thai respect age. Me? Never mind my age, I'm a *farang*. I was plastered with talcum powder paste and soaked to the skin with icewater. All for good luck, all in fun.

On April 17 some monks came from Wat Ma Habut to celebrate the New Year. We fed them, and they sprinkled everyone with water for good luck. There was music and a kind of potluck. The whole affair took place under a tent that was erected for the occasion on the vacant lot beside the bungalow. All our neighbors were there — everybody brought a different kind of food. Great food as usual.

After the monks left, a group of us piled into the back of a pickup truck and headed for Prapradaeng. Everybody in the whole of Thailand seemed to be there. Groups of young boys and girls in the backs of pickups with large water jars, filling up bucket after bucket and soaking anyone and everyone. Water fights between trucks stuck in traffic jams. Throwing water at buses, at motorcycles. Once off the truck, people milled around pouring icewater down other people's backs. And smearing the liquid talcum powder on your face and head. All for good luck, for the New Year. "Plastic bags full of ice water, only one *baht!*" someone shouted. I bought a couple, just for *choke di.*

"Farang," they call, "Tom, Tom, where you go last night?" The words of a hit song. You turned to see who's singing to you, and slosh — you just got a plastic bag full of water on your head. Some even said "Sorry!" before they doused me. Or smeared the white paste on my face. One young girl apologized before throwing iced water all over me. I said, "Thank you for the good luck.

"Not yet," said a voice behind me, and I felt more ice cold water cascading down my back.

Thai gone mad, being themselves, having fun — the Land of Smiles. Once you go to Thailand you never want to go home.

Chapter 5

FUNTOCK!

But by mid-April, all the *farang* had left Thailand. The U.S. and Europe were having pleasant weather again. The girls in the Bier-Kutsche were crocheting and the go-go dancers in Soi Cowboy were shouting *Sawng rawy ha sip baht* — 250 *baht*. The price had gone down. A lot of girls just stood around doing nothing: *Nit noy farang* — few foreigners.

While downtown one day I saw a *farang* leave his wife at the bar and go with a Thai woman short-time. She smiled but you could see the hurt. Actually, Pidang pointed out this action to me. I'd seen girls pick up girls, and couples pick up girls.

Top: *Funtok!* Rain — a chance to wash your shoes.
Bottom: When it rains it pours!

One of my frequent stops downtown at night was the Nana Plaza Disco. Most nights I went there I saw Alee — I usually bought her a drink and gave her 100 *baht* for her taxi home. Sometimes we'd go into the Nana Coffee Shop and eat. But it was a bit expensive compared with the food stands all around the Plaza.

Alee became someone special to me. She told me to *bi bawn* — go home — every time she saw me. "When I see you, my heart does not want to work." She didn't want me to see her pick up a man. The only thing that would save her was money. She was always smiling when she looked at me, but when she looked around the disco she was a huntress. As with so many of the women, I often caught myself thinking, "Too bad she has to work as a prostitute, she's such a nice woman!"

Pidang and I were getting on well again. Things had changed — we were more like friends now. In a way I was truly in love with her. She'd tried to conceive with me but I'd declined. The baby would have been beautiful. I'd eased up about giving her money and she had become more careful. She bought a new money box, a bigger one, in the form of a pig. The last one broke because she spent her time prying money out through the slot with a knife. This one was harder to rob.

She was talking about selling sarongs and bras door-to-door when I left. She finally told me her true age: she was 50. So sad to think of a middle-aged woman still selling her body for a living, but how much could she make selling sarongs and bras? What else could she do?

After breakfast Pidang went to say goodbye to a friend who was off to Germany to work. Her husband, a policeman, would stay home and look after the children while she was away working. This was quite common: many families around there were supported by one member who went abroad to work.

Pidang and I went to the horse races one day. It was mostly a male crowd — there weren't even toilets for the women. Ut and Theo came along — wild excitement at the end of every race. Eight races in all. All bets were with the tote, so the odds were always against you, but it was fun. Sometimes I think the entire Thai way of life can be summed up by the phrase "Good luck!" — *Choke di.*

The rainy season was finally upon us. But the rain — *funtok* — didn't bother anyone. Neither did the thunder and lightning. Thai accept the rain as a matter of course and go about their business.

If you went to the Malaysia Hotel coffee shop, you'd find it reminding you of the 60s. Long hair, dirty jeans — They even had a list on the bulletin board telling who was in jail and for how long. Some people were doing 25 years or more for possession — because they couldn't buy their way out.

Dang bought me a Buddha from a man who was selling them door to door. Luant Po To is the Buddha's name. Everybody said if I wore him around my neck it would bring me *choke di.*

All Thai wear some sort of Buddha around their neck. One man who lived in the neighborhood had about 10 on a chain, for protection and good luck. As soon as I bought one and started wearing it, everybody said, "Oh, you must have a Thai wife." Respect for me increased. Everybody started to talk to me more. And the prices of goods went down. I'd in effect become more Thai. A word to the wise: Buy a Buddha and learn a few words of Thai. Bargains will appear everywhere.

90

Thai ingenuity.

Funtok — rain nearly every day. If one went out one could expect to be drenched. But the Thai just go out and get wet. In the hot season they say *lawn* — hot. Now *Fontok mi di* — Rain no good.

Pidang looked sadder every day. I'd be leaving in ten days. She said nothing, but her eyes spoke volumes. One thing about living with a Thai woman — they do look after you if you look after them. If you lived in a community like the one where I stayed, you'd always be invited, as you pass an open doorway, to *gin khao* — eat rice.

Everything was *biac* — wet from the constant rain. Our clothes were hanging across the inside of our bungalow, over the bed. We used the fan to dry them.

Downtown there were *nit noy farang* and things look sad — the squeeze was on. It's the end of the month and not only does the rent have to be paid, it's also back-to-school time and the women have to buy books and clothing for the kids and pay school fees.

Boa had finally located the father of her baby. A local man went to Hat Yai and saw him in a hotel. The chase was on. He finally came to see Boa and gave her some money. She's in a better mood now.

With all the talk about Hat Yai and me leaving for Hawaii, Si, the woman next door, came by to ask whether Hawaii was as far away as Hat Yai, which was 1,298 km from Bangkok by train. Hawaii is more like 11,000 km away.

Pidang was putting on *nit noy* makeup and dressing nicely these days.

All the neighbors came by at least once a day. When was I leaving? When was I coming back? Would I marry Pidang? Where was I going? I gave geography lessons with my world map. My cat, looked better every day and had been trying to move inside the bungalow. She came in through the window and I chased her out by the door. Cats are the same the world over. Pidang told me not to stroke the cat. *Saca poch,* she says — dirty.

Nok and Won were battling it out again. He called her Pussy Face. "Go work with the *farang* downtown, you lazy buffalo, and make some money!" Nok was a tough woman, but she sat in the doorway of her bungalow and cried bitterly.

She loves Won, but he's only 26 and she's 36 years old. "He's too young for her," Pidang says. "Have a baby with him," she tells Nok, "but don't live with him."

Chapter 6

CHINATOWN

A few weeks before I was to leave, we went to Chinatown with Won. In Chinatown, prices are low. I'd been told that you could pick up a nice-looking woman on Thanon Pantiphap or Soi Phanthachit for as little as 80 *baht* and take her to the Wallicai Hotel nearby. The price of the hotel was included in the 80 *baht*. If you were a *farang* they'd try to get another 100 *baht* from you, but compared to Pat Pong and Soi Cowboy, it was still cheap.

The boyfriends, lovers, pimps and husbands of the girls in this area lived in busses parked across the street from where the girls work. You tell the fellow at the bus which girl you want. He goes and gets her for you and off you go. The lady I met was fascinated by my nose, kept on touching it and giggling.

A street vendor explains the merits of his secret aphrodisiac to passers-by.

Chinatown was also famous for its Lomen Chas — that is, the Chinese teahouses. Of course they're not just teahouses any more. From outside they look like tea shops, barber shops or what have you. Basically, a Lomen Cha is a Chinese Thai-style brothel.

Some have show windows full of women. In some, the girls are displayed in a room at the end of a corridor or just wander around. Most of these Lomen Chas are pretty shabby places. The women are quite pretty in some and of course the price is right: 80 *baht* for one hour in a small cubicle. If you want to drink Chinese tea in your room it's another 20 *baht*. And when they say an hour, they mean an hour — exactly. The women have stopwatches hidden on them somewhere, I'm sure.

Chinatown also has a market for all sorts of other goodies, also pre-recorded videotapes for six dollars, watches for half the price you'd pay in the main tourist areas, Louis Vuitton bags, cameras. Prices here are much lower than elsewhere in Bangkok. A bargain-hunter's paradise.

Lomen Chas aren't frequented by many tourists. Most of their business comes from Thai men. See all those motorbikes in the street? There are a lot parked in the hallways of Lomen Chas.

Pidang went to see her mother who was sick. The day after she left, I went to the Hua Lal lomen cha. I got a pot of tea for 10 *baht*. No air conditioning. The place was a step above some I've seen. The walls of the cubicle were tiled, as was the toilet/shower. It was a Thai-style non-flushing toilet, with a rubber hose attached to a tap for the girls to wash themselves and you. The bed, such as it was, had a red plastic cover, as did the pillow. The girls were lined up on a bench in the hallway. The men walked around and chose the girls they wanted. Boys in yellow T-shirts ran about the place organizing things. As usual, there was a cashier/manager in a wrought-iron cage, keeping track of who was with whom and for how long. An old man limped around carrying tea to the rooms.

"Farang AIDS" is what the first girl who saw me said. "Farang brings AIDS to Thailand" said another.

The men were lying around on the red-plastic-covered beds in the cubicles. The girls would leave the bench in the corridor to walk by the rooms and look in. If the men liked the look of them, they asked them in for tea or beer, and that was that.

A Lomen Cha was one of the cheapest places to get a lover. *Farang* are novelties there.

Some of the girls were beautiful, but of course they spoke no English. There was piped Thai music — *Subri, subri* — "Enjoy, enjoy!", one of the fast moving songs on the Thai hit parade that summer. That song was everywhere, I'll never forget it. The girls were young, 16 to 20. They were at least as attractive as the women who go for four times as much in the tourist districts. The girls in the Hoa Sing Lomen Cha all went to bed at 11 — beauty sleep!

This was interesting but I found myself wanting to get back to Pidang.

Bangkok has hundreds of clinics that can provide first-class medical care 24 hours a day. The fees vary, but 100 *baht* plus, say, 70 *baht* for medication if needed, is a typical figure.

Of course, sexually transmitted diseases are the number one concern of *farang* who visit Bangkok. A blood test for VD should cost no more than 60 *baht*. An AIDS test, 350 *baht*.

The best safeguard against sexually transmitted diseases is abstinence — of course. The second best, about 86% effective, is condoms. "Never leave a bar without one."

Stomach upsets are number two on the list of health hazards for *farang*. Before you buy food from street vendors, give your stomach time to adjust. Never drink tap water. Ask for "safe" water — and it's best to drink bottled water, soft drinks or beer.

If you do get the runs, try Pho Chi pills for a mild upset and Fishing Pills for severe dysentery. Both are Chinese medicine and are available without a prescription.

Top: The writing on the wall.
Bottom: And for those who can't read.

Chapter 7

SOI COWBOY

Located between Soi 21 and Soi 23 Sukhumvit Road was Soi Cowboy. The Soi is full of go-go bars. During the day it looks like a nice family neighborhood: children playing in the street, adults going about their ordinary business. As night falls the street is transformed. The neon lights go on, the girls start showing up for work. One or two bars do have some action during the afternoon, and you can sit outside and enjoy the passing traffic. I met Tuk Tuk in the Old China Hand one afternoon.

She was shouting "F... you!" at anyone who spoke to her, drunk on Mekong whisky and coca cola. At this time of day the bar only gets 100 *baht*. But later on at night, the "bar fine" goes up to 200 or 300 *baht*, depending on the bar.

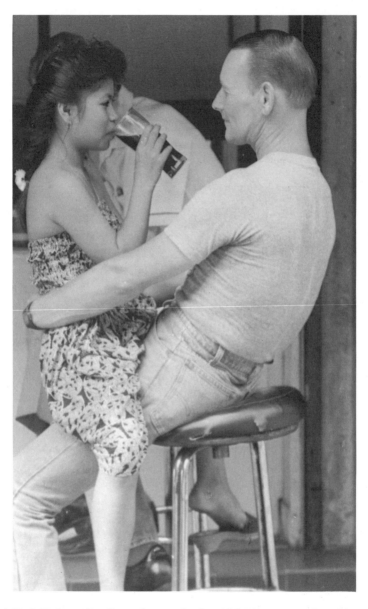

Tuk Tuk with a friend outside the Old China Hand on Soi Cowboy. Her name is actually Tuk, but the *farang* decided it should be Tuk Tuk.

Let me explain this bar fine so it won't sound so outrageous. If you met a woman you wanted to go home with in a go-go bar, you should understand that she worked for the bar and made money for them on drinks. So you paid the bar to spring her from her work. In addition, this practice gave you a bit of protection, since if she decided to give the gold chain from your neck to her mother, you knew where she works.

On the other hand, you are actually giving money away for nothing.

Most of the women here are between 18 and 24 years old. Some men come with the intention of exploring Thailand and never make it any further than Soi Cowboy. Don't worry about not speaking Thai — most of the girls speak a little English, and if they don't, the deal can be worked out using your fingers to indicate the amount. if you don't have a hotel to visit with your chosen beauty, *Mi be li* — never mind. She probably knows one close by that specializes in short-time stays. For your information, 500 *baht* was *Ha rawy baht.* And when you get into the hotel, *ab nam* — take a shower — is the phrase you'll need to know.

There are in all about 15 to 20 bars on the Soi. Most are friendly places. There was one bar, Bien's Place, that seemed to cater only to Thai men. I didn't feel they wanted me to leave, but it didn't seem too lively. Play this one by ear.

A mixed drink in Soi Cowboy cost 40 *baht*. A beer, 25 *baht*. Most places don't have a cover charge. But always ask the price of a "lady drink" — that's where they get you. Look at the bill before you drink. Nod at nobody, or you'll probably end up buying them a drink. And whatever you do, don't ring the bell! You just bought every woman in the bar a drink!

There were no strip shows or any other spectator sports on Cowboy other than go-go dancing, and the girls do not as a rule take off their bikini tops. In most bars the atmosphere is relaxed and if you don't like one set of girls in a bar, just take off and try another. Endless variety.

When I first spoke to Tuk Tuk, she was drinking with a couple of Americans, Gary and Guy. "I can't talk to men if I don't drink," she told me under her breath. "I drink, no problem." Naturally, the more she drinks the wilder she gets. A guy told me he knew her when she first started work at the age of 16. "Shy girl." Now she'll open her legs or mouth for anyone with money — after she gets some alcohol into her. I asked Tuk Tuk why she never tried to marry a *farang*. "I'm free," she said. "No wish to work, no work. I do what I want." The conversation moved to AIDS. Both Americans decided that it all came from the Arabs in the Grace Hotel.

Tuk Tuk says that since she has to work to survive, all she can do is use a condom and get regular checkups. Even if she's risking her life, she has to eat and support her family. That's the bottom line.

The Quiet Spot was just that. Ruby Star swings and has some really fine girls. Jonathan's, Ding Pong and New Crazy Cats were all pleasant places to spend an evening.

The Hare and Hound was a TV non-go-go bar and had some really good-looking girls when I was there. A good place to relax and snuggle.

The standard question from the woman once you get inside a bar was "Where you come from?" If she says "Beer" and you say yes, you just bought her one. "Where you hotel? Where you stay? Where you come from?" It all boils down to the same thing: "Do you want me or not?" If she's talking to you at all, she's interested.

The Thai use your compassion to extract money from you, but I never saw any strong arm work. Just ladies half-naked throwing their arms around a quite ordinary looking man, saying, "Come inside. Please sir! Sexy man!"

Other bars: The Lilac, which boasts, "Over 60 Girls, Eager To Be Your Friends." Valentine, "Where Love Is Waiting," and Darling A Go Go, which boasts 45 naked girls romping and gyrating.

All the girls who work in go-go bars have numbers. Not because they don't have names, but because some of them have the same name. It is easier for accounting to write a number on a piece of paper, which is given to the girls when you buy them a drink. At the end of the evening, they trade in their paper chits for cash: their commission on the drinks they got you to buy. That's right, she didn't drink five orange juices because she was thirsty.

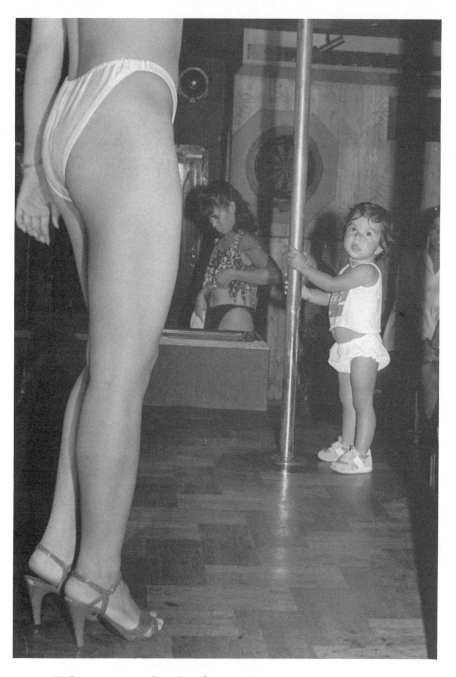

Babysitters are hard to find and expensive in Bangkok.
The same as everywhere else in the world.

Chapter 8:

THE WOMEN

Some women take speed so they can stay up all night and do more business. Also, some of them told me that without the drugs they couldn't do the kind of work they do. Of course, some drink for the same reason. Ut and Nok do — but they frequently get too drunk to go downtown and earn any money.

Ut has worked downtown for 20 years. She's 37. She spends her money on alcohol. Her husband has a good job in the Post Office, but she wanted to earn her own money. An independent woman.

My original impression, in the bars downtown, was that everyone was having a great time.

The longer I hung around and the more attention I paid, the more obvious it was that *nobody* was. This was work in every sense of the word.

If you decide to go home with your lady to her place, be careful: Many men have lost all they own that way. Go when you're sober. Don't carry any money or valuables that you don't want to lose. The family may be more than you can handle: for example, she may have a husband in residence. About 20% of the girls who work downtown were married.

There is a card lady downtown in the Bier-Kutsche. She tells fortunes for the girls — a serious matter. Would they meet a rich *farang* who would marry them and take them away from this work? Forty *baht* a go — not too much for a woman who earns 500 *baht* a trick. She is a kind lady and helps the girls out if they get into trouble, lends them a bit of cash when they are caught short and so on.

Some of the women are truly affectionate. You could walk into a bar, pick one up, and go to bed with her, and find she genuinely likes you.

Others are more cold-blooded. Often a woman marrys a *farang*, gets him to buy a house in Thailand, and then while he is away plays around with the old Thai boyfriend. Of course, sooner or later he finds out and divorces her,

A woman with Oy's looks and charm can easily find a *farang* husband. She keeps contact with two German men. Today she received a letter from one of them. He sent her his love, money and a proposal of marriage. I remarked to her how well she was looking compared to when I first met her. "At first I think too much," she said. "But now I have nice German boyfriend."

which is what she wanted. She now has money and at least half, sometimes all, of the house. It's hard to get money out of Thailand, and often the relatively rich *farang* doesn't bother to try. These girls aren't stupid. As one German man put it, "The less you talk, the less it costs you. Get involved and it will mean money."

I met Alee one night in the Biergarten, an outdoor bar on Soi 7. She was 35, half-Chinese, half-Thai. She said she had been working for only three years, but her English was good — a sign a woman has probably been working for some time. Her main base of operations was the Nana Disco, located in the Nan Hotel, but when there's no business, she hung out at a few other bars. She was married to a *farang*, but has been divorced for several years. "Why can't you manage to marry another *farang?*" I asked. "They have no eyes to see," she replied.

I asked her what she wants in life. She confessed her aim in life was to marry a *farang*, get a house and car and start a business. Give him babies if he wanted them, she adds. Would I be interested? What would she give me in return, I asked. "My life," she said. Actually, it was probably a good deal. She promised she'd stop work as soon as I said so. So she could look after me.

Such a beautiful, loving woman... If only she weren't a hooker!

"I don't like what I do, but I have to do it for my baby," she said sadly. Her daughter was seven years old. She had no mother, no father, one sister. Lived in a 1,500-*baht*-a month room on Rama V with a TV, a radio, a bed, and a wardrobe. Shared a toilet and a bath. She was an honest woman — didn't ask me for money. Once I asked if she wanted some. "Up to you," she said. She dressed very nicely, almost conservatively.

My heart warms when I think of her.

She was trying to save money for when she was old, and for her child's education. But she got sick and couldn't work, so she had to pawn her 10,000-*baht* gold chain. Not an unusual story.

On March 12, at about 4:30 am, I met Noe in the Themae. She was 38 years old and had a daughter of 16. A well-built, remarkably youthful woman. Her English was almost faultless. She was married to a Chinese man, but was now divorced. He bought her some land, but she sold it and bought a house for her mother, who looked after her daughter in a town about 25 miles outside Bangkok. She went out with a young *farang*, a British Embassy official, but his parents got him away from her before she could marry him. She had a boyfriend — an airline pilot who flew in from time to time. She showed me her gold chains and bracelets: one was a New Year's gift from the pilot. She traveled quite a bit. Jakarta, Singapore, Australia. She was a naturally sexy woman. She nearly married an Australian, but she got rid of him when he started getting jealous. She said Thai men were no good. *Mi di* they get drunk, beat up their wives and go butterfly — and some even force their wives to go downtown to make money from *farang*. She lived Thai-style — in a small cubbyhole in a large house — and paid 600 *baht* a month. Communal shower and toilet, of course.

All the money she made she gave to her mother to take care of the house and send the child to school.

I spent the night at Noe's. In the morning, I had breakfast on the upstairs balcony leading to the rooms and was introduced to the other residents.

Soi 22 was near Soi Cowboy, so a lot of the girls who worked there live here. Dong, the woman next door, didn't work with *farang* any more. Didn't have to: her boy friend, an American living in Vancouver, sent her 6,000 *baht* a month. She spent her time listening to

113

old Elvis Presley records, playing with her cat and going shopping. She sipped strawberry cordials with ice and wished she was with her man in Vancouver, where the weather was cool. It was the hot season: 95° Fahrenheit and humid.

The woman on the other side was called Oy. She had a Swiss boy friend. He was 60 years old. She was about 24. He works for a Swiss electric company and has been visiting Thailand for the past seven years. He gives her 10,000 *baht* each time he comes, usually staying about two weeks. From time to time he sent her a gift of money. She also had a Thai husband who lived downstairs, and she still worked downtown. I met Noe a few days later in the Themae. She was off again to Singapore to work. I was glad she left. Noe was the kind of woman who excites me. I could easily have gotten attached to her. Which is exactly what happens to some of the men and why they come home broke and in love and start saving for the next trip to Bangkok.

Not many *farang* in Bangkok in the hot season. Given the price of short time in other countries, and the favorable exchange rate, a Thai woman could make good money by traveling to a foreign land and practicing her profession there.

I asked a woman in the Themae last night, half in jest, to sit on my knee to save space because it was so crowded. She refused. A "nice girl" — you do find a few. A lot of the girls who work in the bars were shy, and some were even prudish. You get used to that.

On another evening, I met Dang. Twenty-seven years old, had a degree in commerce. She had sold her virginity a year ago to pay hospital bills for her mother. What a present for a girl to give her mother!

In Thailand girls are virgins when they marry. Dang was working in a bank, but when her income wouldn't cover her mother's hospitalization, she decided to go downtown. Now she was in business. Got used to the easy money. She told me about one man who went to the hotel with her and in the morning, insisted he'd paid her, though he hadn't. She feels her work was "no good," that she was a "bad girl." About a year ago, she met an American who fell in love with her, proposed marriage, and gave her family 70,000 *baht*. He promised her the good life in America: he'd make her a housewife! He kept on writing to her, asking her to arrange her departure. She never replied — it really didn't appeal to her.

She also made money on the side as a translator. Since she'd gone to a university, she not only speaks good English but writes it too. Most of the women can't write any English, and need someone to carry on their correspondence for them. When the men leave, they often write to the girls and send them money to help them till the next visit. Some women even write to a man saying that he got them pregnant, or that their mother is in the hospital. They'd say anything. Dang writes the letters for them and translates the replies. She is a bright, intelligent woman with dancing eyes. She doesn't smoke or drink or take drugs, and she gave all her money to her family.

By the time we'd finished talking it was six in the morning and the Themae was closing, so we went to a local restaurant. She immediately

Top: Thai women are strong but sensitive.
Bottom: Sign outside a local restaurant.

rushed to the bathroom to take off her makeup. She was afraid someone she knew would see her. She didn't even want to walk with me in the street near the bank where she used to work, in case one of her friends saw her with a *farang*. One day one of her friends did see her in a shop with a client, and she told the friend he was a security man for the Thai Tourist Information Travel Service, where she said she was working.

Dang and I got on very well together. She warned me, though, that if she saw me while she was with a customer she wouldn't be able to say hello.

While sitting drinking *cha lawn* (hot tea) one day in the Themae, one woman asked me, "Do you know why we have to come here? For our families, because our government takes all our money in taxes and doesn't help us when we're old or have children." She'd been to Germany to work. The split was 50-50 with the bar. She had to pay for her own food, but got free lodging in the bar. She complained about the system in Germany. The agent with whom she did her deal kept her passport so she couldn't leave when she wanted to. Not like Thailand: she had to work every day even if she felt sick, usually four or five short-times. If she refused, she was beaten up. The money was good, but no matter how much money she made she never managed to hang on to it.

When it came to getting letters and money from *farang*, some of the girls were true professionals and had a filing system so they could keep track of their boyfriends. If a woman had a file on you, typically it would contain photos of you, letters from you with translations attached, notes on places you'd stayed together, and so forth. When you returned to Bangkok, as over 50% of the visitors do, she met you at the airport. Of course, she checked her file system to make sure she ran up to the right guy and to brush up on the current state of your relationship. When you'd leave, she saw you off at the airport: love and kisses, tears, and a taxi back to work once your plane had taken off. Some girls good, some girls bad.

One *farang* wrote, "So glad I could take you away from work for a week and give you a holiday with me in Chang Mai." I helped the woman compose her response about how much she'd enjoyed her vacation there. "Away from work? I had to make love to him twice a day," she complained.

Many girls made it clear that you were helping them out financially, and it was not a straight cash-for-sex deal. They felt better and so did you. If the woman went butterfly, well, you didn't donate enough to the family and she had to make ends meet.

The girls were not downtown for fun. This was their work and they were good at it. They could make you feel loved — or just a dirty old man. You could decide on that too. Of course, some do truly fall in love with the customers: they're human beings and do have hearts, and intimacy is built into the business. Let's face it, if two people spend a few weeks in bed together, they're going to feel something by the time it's over: love, hate, *something.*

One bar owner put it this way: The girls want money and the men want sex, it was as simple as that. It was *not,* though.

One day in the Grace Coffee Shop Ot who worked the afternoon shift, 1:30 pm to 6:30

pm, said to me, "When I go short-time I usually get 500 *baht*, but for you, 400 *baht*. I like you."

Ot was being a true capitalist. Supply of *farang* was low so sure enough she met the market with the correct response — she lowered the price.

When I declined to go with her, she shook my hand. A minute later, she was dragging a *farang* out the door by the arm. The Saudi looked on longingly: she'd told me, "No go with Saudi men — *saca poch.*" (dirty)

It was not unknown for Saudi to buy a girl of about 15 from her family, for 50,000 to 60,000 *baht* for a five-year period. At the end of the five years the girl was free to come home. Quite a few massage parlors in Bangkok work more or less the same way, though they don't pay as much — only about 40,000 *baht*. An agent will lend that much to some poor family in the north or northeast, and the girl will be sent to Bangkok to work off the loan.

Waiting for work to pay the bills.

On my way out of the Biergarten one night, I met Lek. She had married a Dutchman, but he couldn't handle the fact that she had worked as a bargirl. He tore up all her photos from her previous marriage. Never stopped talking about her past. Used to turn out the light when she was in the shower, to make her hurry to bed. And when she got there, started talking about all the men she must have made it with in the past. She bought him a shirt for Christmas and he tore it up in a rage. She divorced him. "He knew my past before he married me," she shruged. "Why did he marry me in the first place if he couldn't live with it?"

Most of the girls in the New Keynote Bar in Pat Pong got letters from *farang*. Oy showed me one and asked me to translate. It was from an American living in Saudi. He wanted to marry her and bring her home to the USA to meet his family. He sent her 1,000 *baht*, enough to get her high for a while. He didn't know she was a smackhead. Quite a bit of the stuff floating around, so a fair few of the go-go dancers have the habit. They're down on marijuana but have no inhibitions about heroin — I can't imagine why.

There is, of course, other work for the women of Thailand. They could lay bricks or make the steel reinforcing used in building construction, for about 70 *baht* for 12 hours. Or go downtown and sleep with a *farang* and net 500 *baht* for an hour.

Once the girls had accepted the idea of selling themselves, it was hard to go back to ordinary life. Now they were used to money — nice clothes, nice hotels, traveling by taxi and eating out in nice restaurants, going on holiday to Pattaya and the like.

All the girls told me they didn't like the work. But all said they loved money. Some of them pissed it away: one woman, who worked the Malaysia Hotel, spent all the money she'd saved and even pawned her gold chain to play video games. And had to go back to work again.

The girls had nearly all been in love once. "I may like a man a lot but I can never love again," they said.

By the way, it was sometimes hard to tell who was working and who was not. Most of the women in the street wouldn't even look at you — that was Thai style — but if one did want to get to know you, don't worry, she'd make it clear.

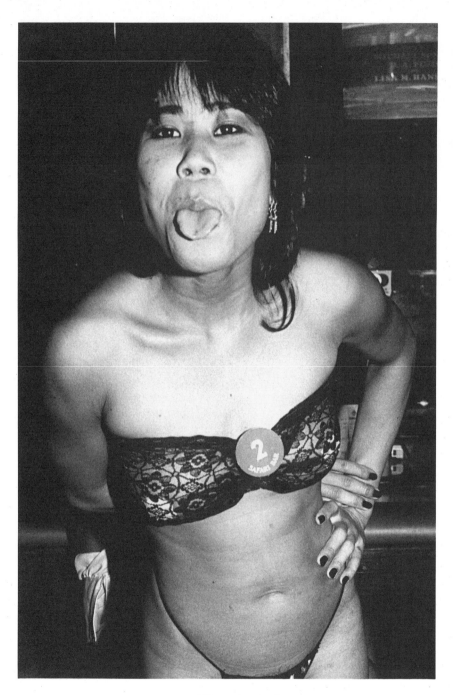

Wrong price!

There were girls who work for large department stores who would be quite willing to go out with you. However, these were not hookers. You'd have to court one for a considerable length of time before you could even hold hands.

One of my regular friends in the Themae was Wy Pawn. She was 34 years of age and had worked in Germany for three months and made 200,000 *baht*. She had a 600,000-*baht* house. No mother, no father, two children. One was going to be in the 'Big Police'. She had just come back from a three-month tour of Thailand with her German boyfriend. She liked working in Germany. Each man got 20 minutes, come or no come. He got kicked out — and she still got paid. Not like Thailand, where the competition was too keen for her to get away with that kind of thing.

Indeed, when the *farang* got scarce in April, I saw two Thai girls battle it out blow for blow outside the Themae one night.

A lot of women work downtown because their husbands insist on it. Not exactly a pimp sort of arrangement, but not all that different. If they don't go, they may be in for a beating. Pidang says that was why she would never marry a Thai man.

"Work for him while he sit at home and do nothing? No way!"

Of course, not all the girls had a man in the background. That didn't mean you didn't have to pay them: for a small fee they could get an acquaintance to beat you up or bump you off. But don't worry, you'd only get trouble if you asked for it.

Some of the girls paid not only to have their faces made up, but also for shots to swell up their skins so they'd have fewer wrinkles and look younger. They wanted to look beautiful for you — and extend their working life.

Chapter 9:

DEATH IN THAILAND

When someone dies in Thailand, a special day is set aside for the members of the family to stay at home and do their crying. Friends come by and commiserate with the bereaved. People still die at home, so that the body is sent to the *wat*. At the *wat* there are two alternatives: either the body is embalmed and kept for a year until all the relatives can be brought together for the cremation, or that ceremony takes place immediately. Whatever the case, on one night there was Thai dancing. "Thai dancing" was not so much a dance as a play with talking, punctuated by dancing. One I saw told the story of a young schoolgirl who "goes butterfly" with another woman's husband and gets pregnant.

Traditional Thai dancing at the local *wat* is more like a morality play punctuated by screaming and yelling.

Lots of screaming and yelling — and beating. In fact, it was more like a slice of Thai life onstage. Some of the dance groups were supported by the King. The young boys and girls I saw were between 14 and 19 years old. They were orphans and the monks at a *wat* looked after them and made sure they went to school. From time to time people in the audience went up to the stage and gave money to the dancers.

The following night a portable projector and movie screen arrived at the wat and it was movie night. Everybody sat cross-legged on the ground and vendors with carts came to sell food and drink. You don't even have to miss any of the movie while you buy your favorite dish.

The embalming takes place in front of everybody at the *wat*. When the embalmer is finished, he extends the right arm of the corpse and *lot nam sop* begins. This is water being poured into the hand of the dead person so he or she will be clean for the journey.

Then the burning, *pow sop.*

Once the crying is over, people do not talk to the relatives and friends about the dead person. That might sadden them.

The funeral I attended was like a wake, with dances and speeches and family photographs.

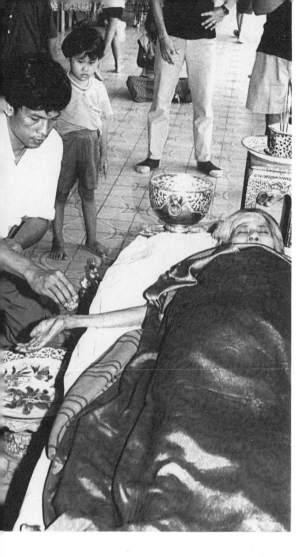

Lot Nam Sop — At a Thai funeral, water is poured into the hand of the deceased by close relatives. This is a ceremonial and ensures that the dead person will be "clean for the journey."

The dead woman's son even brought me out on the floor in front of the crowd and kissed me. To kiss a male *farang* and be alive is better than to be dead.

Afterwards I went to Biergarten Soi 7, Sukkumuit Road, an open-air bar with a nice selection of girls. They're free-lancers, so you don't have to pay the bar. I have seen some really gorgeous girls here. This was a good place to meet the lady or ladies who you want to share your bed with while you're in Bangkok. They expect about 500 *baht* for their company

Unfortunately AIDS is making the funerals of young girls who work in bars, more and more frequent.

Chapter 10

THE MEN

Later I passed the Nana Disco, located on Soi 4, off Sukhumvit Road, opposite the Nana Plaza entertainment center. More expensive than the regular bars, but it was a nice place. The girls here want at least 500 *baht*. They're mostly dressed conservatively and it was hard to tell that this was a pickup disco. In fact, three Western women came in one night and stayed half an hour before they caught on. They left looking terribly upset.

The drinks were 65 *baht*. The sound system was of top quality and the band was good. When I went I felt it was one of the best discos in town, with some of the finest-looking women.

I met two black Americans in the Bier-Kutsche. They say they love all the girls. One

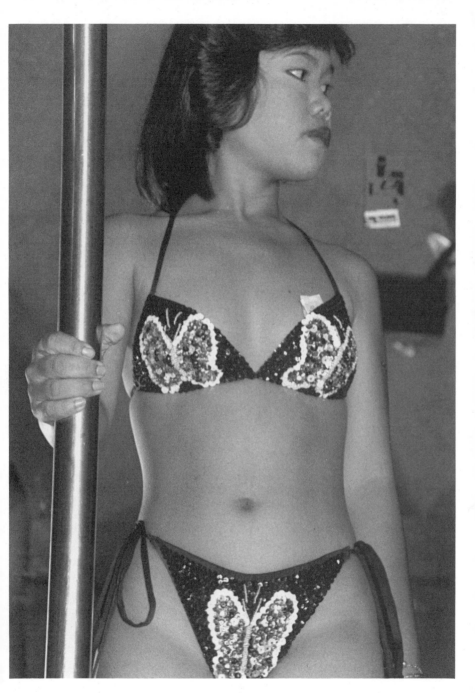

Going Butterfly?

135

even married a Thai woman, but she continued working while he was away and sending her money, so he found another. He gave his girl 1,000 *baht* to repair the roof on her parents' house and sends her money every month from Saudi, where he works as a programmer.

Three young American men in their early twenties walked into the Bier-Kutsche one night. Two were already with Thai girls. They ordered three beers each and three rounds of tequila and lime, which they soon polished off. They seemed out of place even before they drank the tequila, but by the time they had finished the drinks they were not only the youngest people in the bar but the drunkest and loudest.

Having drunk up his courage, the one without a woman went over to the other side of the bar and brought back a good-looking Thai with him, shouting to his friends at the top of his voice, "She doesn't speak much English, but I don't care." After about ten minutes he left his friends at the bar and returned about 15 minutes later with the woman to announce to his friends, "I came! I came!"

The Saudis like to visit Thailand to misbehave and do all the things they can't do at home. In fact, close to 60,000 go to Thailand

Top: The girls who work the bars, Pat Pong and Soi
Cowboy, often arrive at work by motorbike taxi. Visitors
with strong hearts can try their hand at being motorbike
passengers too.
Bottom: The Saudi go to Thailand to do all the things that
are forbidden in their country.

every year. Most wind up at the Grace Hotel Coffee Shop. Some bars have signs in Arabic refusing entry to Saudis. They like to fight when they get drunk. Some girls will not go with them. They have to pay a higher price to get the same as other *farang.* In fact, there were two words for foreigner in Thailand: *farang* and Saudi. Crude, one woman said. Another commented, "Saudi men — Saudi stink!" These were working girls, and if the price was right they'll put up with quite a lot.

Anyway, if you don't like Saudis don't go to the Grace Hotel.

The Australian I met in the Bier-Kutsche couldn't stop talking about "queers" — and "maculine women." Strange those Aussies. He went off to Soi Cowboy after he'd finished one drink, saying that all the women were the same anyway. Probably something to do with living Down Under.

The Nana Hotel Disco is where I met an American working for the U.S. State Department in Bangladesh. Sixty-two years old and divorced. He has a girl friend who works behind the bar. She lets him pay her rent and buy her presents, but won't take cash. While we were talking, a black man, about six foot two, walks over to us. My protection, says the State

Department worker. He has a black belt in karate. How nice to know that Uncle Sam is working in a pickup bar in Bangkok.

The men send money to the girl of their dreams in Thailand. These were the women they had the time of their life with, and were easy to love. They don't feel as if they're sending money to a prostitute, but to a friend who was poor and who lives in a developing country, to help her and her family financially. She doesn't bitch and moan about his drinking or tell him her problems with the kids or the daily problems of running the house. To keep her happy, all he has to do is send her money. She'll write back and love him forever — or at least until he stops sending money. When he is in town he can have all the sex he can handle — No "I have a headache." The exchange rate makes him a millionaire. Paradise.

Top: Her hand may be in the right place, but is her heart?
Bottom: Who's the boss?

Quite a few men do marry the girls. But more often than not it doesn't work out. Some of course, marry their girls, bring them back home to Germany and put them to work again at their old trade in bars. Others try to make a go of it. But once they're in the Western world, the environment changes everything. The man has to go to work every day. He is no longer a rich *farang*. And they can't go out drinking and dancing every night. The woman is exposed to the Western female way of thinking. The economic realities as well as the social ones bear down on them. The girls are often not happy with the food and climate of their new home. In addition, if there is no Thai community nearby, the woman is alone in the world. She may end up as a social outcast because of her race. All these factors put stress on the relationship.

Of course, sometimes the man wants to marry and the woman doesn't. Tuk Tuk said she was free the way she was... could come and go to work as she pleased... no man to be supported and tell her what to do.

On a trip to Pat Pong I met Roo Reid. He was a 29-year-old Englishman who went to an English public school. He was writing a book about Pat Pong. Fiction. An Englishman who comes to Bangkok and goes down the drain. He winds up in a sex show and, due to his heroin habit, can't get it up any more. He eventually commits suicide. Roo has gone through 40 women so far. "Only one of them was any good," he comments.

Roo has been working as a barker outside the New Keynote Club in Pat Pong. He tells anyone who'll listen which bars were ripoffs and which were not. For his trouble he was told by the Thai boys who do the barking in another club that if he continued they'd kill him. He was beginning to sound like the main character of his book.

One night in the Biergarten on Soi 7, Bob, a 58-year-old American, was sipping his beer. A friend had paid him back a $3,000 loan and the check was good, so when his wife left Santa Barbara for two weeks to visit her son and daughter-in-law in Illinois, Bob was off to Bangkok. He kept telling everybody in earshot that if she ever found out she'd kill him. Apparently he'd forgotten all about the stamps on his passport. He also told us about all the money he'd made when he sold his house. This chap was really surprised when the German beside him suggested that since he'd made so much money he should buy us all a drink. He did, the twit, but with a miserable expression on his face.

The next day I stopped by the Grace and met John and Michael, two French men from Paris They had been in Bangkok on a business trip and with their wives, but somehow had been bumped from the return flight and left here alone. They were leaving that evening at nine. They kept one of their two rooms and time-shared it for two-hour stretches, running in and out with women. I pointed out some of the girls I knew. John smacked his lips. They had a competition going to see who could sleep with the most girls before they left. John mentioned

Top: Sidesaddle is the way most of the girls ride on
motorbikes. Even policemen give their wives and girl
friends rides this way.
Bottom: Five million inhabitants of Bangkok — and all on
your bus going downtown.

the impressive cleanliness of the girls — "always
ab nam."

Michael chose a wild-looking character in a
halter top and a miniskirt. She sat down opposite him and spread her legs to let him have a
quick look. His mind was made up instanta-
neously. Off he went, almost running out the
door.

Sean O'Brien was sitting beside me, watch-
ing all the action. He'd caught a dose of VD on
his first night in Bangkok. "They say an
Irishman is the only man in the world who will
step over a naked woman for a bottle of beer,"
he says, with a tear in his eye. "That's what you
get for agreeing with the Pope about the use of
condoms."

I meet Roo Reid from time to time in Pat
Pong. He's living his book now. The girls, the
drugs, the whole show. He's not working onstage yet, but it's only a matter of time.

On one of my visits to the Grace Hotel Coffee
Shop I chatted briefly with a Saudi. He was sitting at the bar looking stoned, listening to his
Walkman and gulping down Mekong whisky and
Coke. He was talking nonstop about Thai
women. "Dirty bitches," he said thickly, "dirty.
All dirty." He removed his headphones and I
heard Bob Marley singing, *"Stand up for your
rights."* He repeated Marley's words, adding, "I

drink, I smoke. But never go with the girls. Dirty." Sounds just like a Thai woman talking about Saudi men. I wonder if he knows that.

Some men who come to Thailand are really unhinged by the freedom and make fools of themselves. I have seen two *farang,* surrounded by lovely women, fight it out over a fairly ordinary one. (When the fight began, one girl shrieked, "Oh, *farang* boxing!") They disgraced themselves, not just in front of the Thai women, but in front of males from all over the world.

A friend of mine in the Themae said hi to me one night. She was with a man. He got so upset that he refused to eat the food he'd bought. He sat there sulking like a child as she tried to persuade him to eat up his food like a good boy. It must have been his first time in Thailand.

As one woman put it, "A man who goes with a girl in Thailand must have a strong heart. He has to understand that the girls are working."

One night at the DC-10 Club, in the Nana Plaza Entertainment Center on Soi 4, off Sukhumvit Road, I met Jacques. He had met a girl there and brought her with him for a tour of Thailand, but he'd run out of money. So he could no longer support her. She was back at work. "I

Perhaps it was not Helen of Troy's face that launched a 1000 ships after all. *Farang in Thailand fight over this.*

147

don't like it," he said, "but what can I do? She
has to live, you know!"

The Simon Cabaret, performed by *kathoy* — "lady's boy." *Kathoy* were told by the Buddha before they were born that they could never love a man or a woman in this life, only in the next one after they die and are cremated. They are very much accepted by Thai society. After all, you may be a *kathoy* in your next life.

Chapter 11:

PATTAYA

Located about 150 kilometers south of Bangkok, this is Thailand's Riviera. When you are in Pattaya, it's hard to believe you're still in Thailand. Of course, the availability of women is the most obvious clue.

The girls do a lot of traveling between Bangkok and Pattaya, especially when an American Navy ship pulls in for R&R. This is where family men from all over the world get away from their families to go on those notorious "sex tours." There are bars easily the size of football fields, full of willing and able ladies. They cater to all tastes and desires. English is the primary language spoken here, and it's difficult to find a sign written in Thai script. The

Top: This is #41 at the "Baby A Go Go" in Pattaya. She has just finished "performing" erotic dancing on stage. Upon getting down from the cat walk she joins her hands Thai style, a sign of respect for Buddha and herself.
Bottom: The go-go girls work hard for a living and the competition for *farang* is fierce. A newcomer gets a helping hand with her makeup.

male Disneyland of Asia, or perhaps of the whole planet. One gigantic pickup bar.

Prices in Pattaya are higher than in Bangkok. It's a 24-hour town and many bars stay open all night.

When a ship arrives and discharges 8,000 men on shore leave, the girls are a bit overworked. They may go short-time as many as seven or eight times in a day. Speed helps them stay awake. The girls come here to make their fortune. The women in Pattaya, like the women in Bangkok, get lots of letters from lonely sailors. "Sorry to hear your grandmother is sick," wrote one man. "Here are 2,000 *baht* to help her out." The woman was cleaning up — he wasn't the only man she'd written to, and her grandmother had been dead for some time. The victim mentioned that he was saving up his money to come back and see her again soon — his only true love.

The place has its share of go-go bars and places where girls can do just about anything with their privates. Like smoke cigarettes. Like blow whistles. Like shoot off dart guns to pop balloons. There's even an intellectual one who uses a pen to write love letters — just tell the girl your name and she begins a composition especially for you. What a souvenir!

A *kathoy* - lady boy performs at the Simon Cabaret, Pattaya.

Blue Heaven Bar is a good spot for nice women. Baby A Go Go is the ideal bar for a snuggle.

Caligula has women who smoke cigarettes from strange places.

All the bars I've mentioned here are located in the Diamond Beach area.

The going price to spring a lovely lady from a go-go bar is 300 *baht*. Having asked one to tell me how much help she needed for her family, I was told it was entirely up to me. Yet the amount we finally agreed on was 500 *baht*. It's worth your while to find out whether your choice is a freelancer, because if she is you don't have to pay the bar fine. You can also, between lovely ladies, see Thai boxing, go to a restaurant, hire a motorcycle or jeep and go for a ride, and live like a millionaire for a while.

One place you should go is the Simon Cabaret, to see the *Kathoy* (Lady Boy) Show. The performers are all men who have had sex changes. They're astonishingly beautiful. And the show is not only erotic but very funny.

Pattaya has had a few incidents, so be careful with your money, your personal belongings, and your person.

And always remember that these women work to entertain you so they can support themselves and their families. They are human beings with intense feelings.

One of the younger dancers at the Caligula go-go bar in Pattaya.

Chapter 12

MASSAGE

You can get every conceivable sort of massage in Thailand. The two main types are sensual and traditional. (Yes, there's still traditional massage in Bangkok!) I'll list the best establishments I visited, covering the traditional places first.

The Marble House, 37/18-19 Soi Surawong Plaza, behind the Pizza Hut Lane at the Rama IV end of Surawong Road (phone 235-3519). At the Marble House they believe in a holistic approach: both physical and spiritual. The rate is about 160 *baht* per hour. No funny stuff here, just good clean massage. Open 10 am to midnight.

Wat Pho, near the Grand Palace, is the spiritual center of Thai massage. You can get a massage and also study massage here. The courses last two to three weeks and cost about 2,500 *baht.*

Siam Yansa, 163/13-17 New Arun-Amarin Road (phone 424-3110), has traditional massage specialists. The rate is 80 *baht* an hour. Food and drink are available downstairs. For those who want a Thai-style experience.

If you want sensual massage, there are all sorts of establishments, and all sorts of prices. The women are astonishingly beautiful in most of these places. The choice of one to rub your back — or your front — is not easy. Of course, if it's too much trouble, you can just shut your eyes and pick a number between 1 and 100... but window shopping is more usual. Especially in a massage parlor with a hundred girls standing behind the window, just waiting for you to choose them.

La Cherie, 25-35 Surawong Road (phone 233-9650-2), in the Pat Pong area, is one of those places with private air-conditioned rooms. The girls know how to manipulate any part of your body you want manipulated. The price is between 600 and 800 *baht.*

The Atami, 1573 New Phetchaburi Road (phone 252-8907-8), is in the same class.

Chao Phaya II is a luxurious place where you can feel like a film star. The rooms are well-decorated and clean. The rate is 500 *baht* for the girl and the room. It is located on Soi Sir Ayodtaya, around the corner from the Century Hotel. They have Thai and *farang* food, as well as live music. And the girls — you'll dream for the rest of your life about the ones you nearly chose. They perform just about any type of service you can imagine and a few that will probably surprise you. These are professionals at their work.

There is also Chao Phaya I, on the same block.

Some of these massage parlors really have beautifully decorated rooms. Check them out before you pay, though.

Chavala is for those who like "smoking" — Thai/English for oral sex.

Remember, always ask the price first! Don't stay if you feel you're being overcharged. Go to a few first, then decide on the place and the person you want to massage you.

By the way: The cabdriver gets a cut, so if you can get rid of him before you go inside, you'll save some money, perhaps enough to give a handsome tip to the lady of your choice to help her.

Most hotels supply girls as well as rooms. The average price range for a room and a girl is 150 to 200 *baht.*

There is even a lane off Thanon Wisut Kasat where a quickie is 50 *baht.* These are private bungalows. Mind you, the women may be less attractive than those who charge more.

A not-so-bad place is the Mali Garden Hotel, on Thanon Bam Pung Puang, #432 Soi 12. There is a room full of young women on the second floor. A few more sit on benches in the corridor, sipping Cokes and smoking cigarettes while they wait for customers. The price is 180 *baht,* which includes both the girl and a room with mirrored walls and ceiling. She shares the money 50-50 with the Chinese owners. Not by any means the worst place I have seen and there's a good selection of cheerful and pretty women — beauty-contest-winners. Of course, conversationally they may be less interesting than the girls who work regularly with *farang*, but on the other hand they are a full 300 *baht* cheaper. And what smiles!

You can also try Hotel 25 or Hotel 4 on Soi Phaya Nak.

These women work hard to earn their living. Lower prices reflect the absence of *farang* customers.

Chapter 13

THE GRACE HOTEL

At the Grace Hotel, located on Soi 5 Sukhumuit, the coffee shop is for Saudis. In fact, it is the Saudi Disneyland. There's even an in-house clinic in case you catch some nasty disease.

Indeed, the security system in the Grace is the best. If you go upstairs with a girl, she won't be able to leave until security phones you in your room to make sure "everything is all right," which means you haven't been robbed. Women have been known to hide gold chains and cash in odd parts of their anatomy.

One night I was offered a sixteen-year-old girl in the Grace. I passed on that. Several nights later I saw a sixteen-year-old "woman"

These women helped
build this house for 70
baht a day.

there. Someone had obviously accepted the offer, so she was now wearing makeup, smoking cigarettes and chatting with Saudi men. I hope the lady who offered her to me taught her how to save her money — if so, some day she can get out of the life.

If a woman goes to the coffee shop on her own, she has to buy a 40-*baht* chit to get in. Once inside, she can use her chit to buy a drink. For men, entry is free!

The Grace is where the Saudi come to misbehave... lift up girls' dresses, squeeze their breasts, abuse them in various ways. Saudi like to fight each other, and the Grace is the scene of an occasional drunken brawl.

Although a lot of girls claim not to go with Saudi, a lot of them actually do, because Saudi pay well. Most *farang* don't want to go with girls who go with Saudi and the girls know this, so they will arrange a rendezvous in a Saudi's room so *farang* won't see them leaving the coffee shop with him. It takes money to pay the rent.

On the other hand, the Saudis love to go with a girl who goes with a *farang*. Status thing, I guess.

The Ambassador Cocktail Lounge in the Ambassador Hotel between Soi 11 and Soi 13 on Sukhomvit Road is for the more affluent — 85 *baht* a drink. Here the men tend to just give the girl what they feel is the right price. Themae-style bargaining really isn't done.

Chapter 14

PAT PONG

Pat Pong is the biggest entertainment center in Bangkok. The prices here are higher than anywhere else, but the girls are indeed beautiful. Sin Alley is its affectionate name. And here you can buy enough affection and love to provide you with a lifetime of dreams. The street is owned by the Pat Pong family — a nice piece of income property. This is actually the business district of Bangkok, so you find not only lonesome men from all over the world, but Thai businessmen as well. Most of the girls come from the impoverished northeastern corner of Thailand, a region covering about one-third of the country. For the most part, the money they earn goes straight home. Back in the Sixties, Pat Pong was just a few bars. It's grown explosively in the past

164

20 years. Back in 1969, an enterprising young man named Rick Menard, owner of the Grand Prix, started go-go dancing in Thailand. (The first dancer, by the way, was not a Thai girl but an Englishwoman.) Then came the Vietnam War, and the GIs who visited Bangkok for R&R. The place took off then, and hasn't had a slump since then.

Go-Go Bar Etiquette — Some Dos and Dont's:

Ask the price before you buy.
Ask the time of the show if they have one - Pat Pong especially
Get the price for a lady's drink too.
Look at the bill before you drink.
Don't ring the bell unless you want to be a hero and buy every woman in the bar a drink.
Don't nod unless you know what is being said
Ask before you take photos.
Bars do not usually employ strong arm tactics — but be cool.
To get the lady of your dreams out of the go go bar, away from work and home with you, expect to pay a "bar fine" of at least 300 baht. Your special lady will probably ask for 500 baht. If you do have any problem in Pat Pong — and I certainly didn't — pay the bill and look for the tourist police nearby. You'll get all your money

back plus enough to buy an extra beer. It will be unusual if you get mugged, but it happens once in a while.

There are plenty of vendors in the street selling souvenirs and what have you, and one of the best bookshops in Bangkok, the Bookseller at 81 Pat Pong Road.

Pat Pong is a safe place — but my advice is to stick with the crowd.

The Rome Club is a sort of gay/lesbian bar, frequented by straight *farang* women as well. There's a transvestite show there every night around 11 pm.

Of course, in these days of AIDS, you might just want to be a spectator. The 30 downstairs bars are strictly go-go — but upstairs there are the risque "exotic" shows.

Happy hour is from 6 to 9 PM, with beer at 35 *baht*. After that it's 65 *baht*. But ask if you're not told the price — otherwise it could be anything — and check your bill before you drink.

You don't have to buy a woman a drink, but since her livelihood depends on how many drinks you buy, be courteous — expect to pay double the regular price. The girls get paid the standard 2,000 to 2,500 *baht* a month — plus tips, plus commissions on the drinks, and of course if you take one home she gets money from you for her family.

The King's Castle Bar is supposed to have the most beautiful girls. That's probably true.

While you walk around looking from the outside, you'll be begged to go inside each place: "Live show, live show, see sexy show... Sir... love inside, Sir... nice lady for you!"

The action is really in the upstairs bars.

Pink Panther is a good spot — and Pussy Alive and Pussy Galore — the names speak for themselves. Cleopatra has an upstairs show that will make your eyes jump out of your head.

Safari, or Casanova — some beautiful and interesting women work here.

The sound systems in most bars are very good and very loud, but they're not a problem. If you wish to communicate with a woman and don't speak any Thai, you'll feel at home using sign language. Everyone else will be doing the same.

The Full of Love Bar is an interesting place. Ladies here tend to put their heads in your lap a lot. A friend of mine calls it the Free Sample Bar.

Of course, all the non-go-go upstairs sex shows are illegal and every bar has an alarm button outside the door, to be pressed in case someone spots a raid on the way. It does happen occasionally that someone decides the 40,000 *baht* or so per month paid in hush money is not enough.

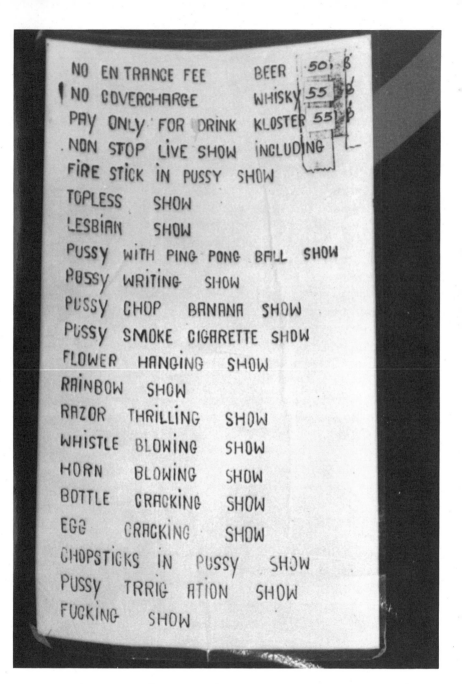

NO ENTRANCE FEE   BEER   50 ฿
NO COVERCHARGE   WHISKY 55 ฿
PAY ONLY FOR DRINK   KLOSTER 55 ฿
NON STOP LIVE SHOW   INCLUDING
FIRE STICK IN PUSSY SHOW
TOPLESS   SHOW
LESBIAN   SHOW
PUSSY WITH PING PONG BALL SHOW
PUSSY WRITING   SHOW
PUSSY CHOP BANANA SHOW
PUSSY SMOKE CIGARETTE SHOW
FLOWER HANGING SHOW
RAINBOW SHOW
RAZOR THRILLING SHOW
WHISTLE BLOWING SHOW
HORN BLOWING SHOW
BOTTLE CRACKING SHOW
EGG CRACKING SHOW
CHOPSTICKS IN PUSSY SHOW
PUSSY TRRIG ATION SHOW
FUCKING SHOW

Barkers carry these hand flyers around to entice you into
the establishment where they work.

168

When the alarm sounds, everyone gets dressed. The snake is returned to his cage, the lady stops writing love letters with the felt pens, the bottles are opened at the bar and not onstage. The police arrive to find a fairly innocent scene.

Sex show personnel are paid 100 *baht* per go — not exactly a star's salary.

The Nana Plaza Entertainment Center is a two-story plaza full of bars. It is located on Soi Nanatai/Soi 4, off Sukhumvit Road. The DC-10 Club, one of the bars there, pays about 10,000 *baht* a month rent plus electricity, plus about 2,000 *baht* a month for police security. The girls here are between 18 and 21. The men tend to be in their fifties. If you want to "take a lady," it will cost you 300 *baht* for the bar and 500 *baht* for the lady. The bar price drops to 200 *baht* after midnight, and you can always try to arrange to meet your future lover after the bar closes. Some girls will, some won't. The price for the lady, too, goes down as the night wears on. You have to work it out with the individual. The girls in go-go bars move around a lot. Remember this is not some sort of a game for these women. The amount you pay for their company will decide whether they can pay the rent or buy their children school books.

Chapter 15

DOING THE ROUNDS

One night one of the girls was so drunk that it took two girls to get her into a chair outside the bar where she worked. As I watched, one of the flower vendors, who go around from bar to bar trying to get *farang* to buy roses for the girls, came onto the scene — to help. What he did was help himself to the money in the girl's pocket. Be forewarned that there are some fast pickpockets in Thailand.

At the Asian Intrigue Bar you can see Thai boxing, only the opponents are scantily-clad girls. The Woodstock Bar has some fine-looking ladies and is a good place to watch videos on a giant screen.

Sexy Cat and the Farang Connection have some glamorous ladies, who will shower with you before giving you a nice massage.

I met Da one day in the Grace Hotel. She was 32 and had been working for three years. She had met a Japanese and married him. He bought her a house in Thailand, then went back to Japan, where he somehow changed his mind about spending the rest of his life with a former bar girl who already had a child. She went to visit him in Japan but he sent her back to Thailand, saying he'd follow. But he never came, and never sent any money. So off she went to look for him in Japan. She found him in his office with two women. She broke the windows, screamed at him, returned to Thailand and went to work in the Grace. She must have loved him, because she never stopped talking about her broken heart. "You break a cup you glue it back together, it holds water. But not same!"

Right now she's on speed so she can work long hours. "If I stay at home I think too much." She makes 500 *baht* short-time, about three times a day.

She talked to me for about three hours. Hugged me and kissed me on the cheek. Pointed out a man smoking a pipe at the bar, who lived in a German Embassy house. She was there a few days ago. He used a vibrator on her. The time before that, there was a 250-*baht* doctor bill, because the man was so well endowed.

Her rent is 3,500 *baht* per month. Most of her money was sent home to her mother, who looked after her baby in a town near Bangkok.

As we talked, her sister came by and tried to persuade her to go to Singapore to work. "You stop here, you die here," she said. "You know, I told my sister she has two arms two legs, a pussy, is not sick and has a good body. Go to work and make money. If you believe anything anyone says here, you are sick." Good advice.

The five gold chains around Da's neck were from three Swiss, a Finn, and a Frenchman. Some of them even sent her money from time to time. The gold chains are an investment. if things get bad or she could not work due to sickness the chains would be pawned for the needed cash.

I excused myself and went out to the bathroom. As I came back, she was leaving the bar arm-in-arm with a *farang,* and so was her sister. Well, business is business. But she'd given me three hours of her time for the price of a drink. She must have liked me a lot. The girls make more money in Singapore.

While we were chatting she told me about the man who went into the Grace for a few beers on his way home and was persuaded by a girl to go short-time. They went to the Playboy

173

Hotel. When he woke up six hours later, his 6,000-*baht* gold chain and his watch were gone, and so was his cash: 40,000 *baht*. The figure is probably inflated, but there's no smoke without fire. He was drugged in his hotel room.

If the police do find the girl she'll go to jail — but it's also possible for her to buy her way out, in which case the police will tell the *farang* they couldn't find her.

Today was mail day in the Bier-Kutsche. When I looked in around six o'clock, the girls were reading their letters from *farang*. Two were trying to decide whether they'd gotten letters from the same man. They showed me... looked like the same handwriting to me... But the real question was who got money?

The Ambassador Hotel on Sukhumvit Road near Soi 11 has its fair share of ladies outside on the street, but be forewarned that a lot of "lady boys" are working the area. The choice is yours. The Thai call them *kathoy*.

When you bargain, remember that some Thai think *farang* have too much money, and think they're doing you a favor by lightening your load. They'll call you a "Cheap Charlie" if you refuse to be taken in, but if you pay too much they'll think you're stupid.

The best way to get around downtown is the bus. Only two *baht* for the non-air-conditioned variety. Those are the most fun. If you want to get close to Thai this is the way. Most of the six million people in Bangkok seem to be on your bus. Some of the conductors are female. The little woman who, instead of shouting *Pai* (Go!) to the driver when it was time to go, blew a football whistle in everybody's ear. What a lady! When everyone was being thrown from one end of the bus to the other under fierce and frequent braking, she balanced perfectly without even hanging onto the overhead hand rail. Probably takes Thai boxing lessons in her spare time.

The numerals are western script on all buses. But the names of destinations are only in English on air conditioned busses.

Having heard about the Great Ambassador Hotel's Flamingo Club, I decided to go see it. The light show was fantastic. The place was half the size of a football field and full of rich young Thai. It cost 100 *baht* to get in, which included two drinks. Not really a pickup joint, but it was possible to meet a woman here.

If you get lucky, you might even meet a charming Thai lady at a bus stop or on the bus. The #2 bus runs all night. The #119 bus, which runs along Sukhumvit Road, will get you from Soi Cowboy to the Bier-Kutsche and Grace Hotel, Soi 3, Biergarten, Soi 7, Pat Pong, Surawong Road, Silom Square, Lomphini Park, to the Bangkok Railway Station beside Chinatown — and all for two *baht*. The best tour in town and the cheapest.

The Themae opens at 12 midnight. At this time there are a few girls around. They've probably shown up early because they want to do a couple of short-times in one night. They do one before 2 am, then go back to try their hand again when the place starts to fill up with men who didn't score before the bars closed. The girls who didn't get a *farang* in Soi Cowboy, Nana Plaza or Pat Pong come to the Themae at this time too. By 2:30 am the place is jammed with women of every possible size and shape. The choice is overwhelming. Madonna screams from the jukebox that she feels like a virgin, touched for the very first time, and some of the girls at the bar are trying to persuade first-timers in Bangkok that they feel that way too. When Madonna gets around to telling everybody she's a material girl, that sounds more realistic to the old-timer on a return visit, who says firmly, *Sam rawy baht* (400 *baht*) to the girl in the faded blue jeans.

You don't pay the bar at the Themae, but you are expected to buy drinks there. If you start to chat with a girl, it's only polite to buy one for her. By Western standards the drinks are not expensive.

If you go to only one place in Bangkok, go to the Themae. Every age group, racial mix, and sexual persuasion turns up here: a real hot spot. Not the most lavish of places but the action is the hottest: when they play "The Final Countdown" on the jukebox, they have the right idea. This is where everyone goes when every other place is closed and they have to score. Some girls won't come here; they say they hate it. But when the rent is due or the baby needs clothes or school fees have to be paid, they come. Not to be missed. A classic coffee shop. Oh, they do serve coffee once in a while — it's a special order.

The price of a lover goes down as the morning approaches. Of course the girls will ask for as much as they think they can get, but this is an excellent place to bargain it out, because they've got nowhere else to go. After 2 am, 400 *baht* is a reasonable price.

The money you give the woman is between you and her. The amounts I've given are only approximations in round figures. You decide with her.

178

The Themae is on Sukhumvit Road just around the corner from the Grace Hotel. Ask any taxi driver. He will know how to get there.

There is another all-night coffee shop, like the Themae, in Pat Pong. It has the same array of beauties to choose from. You'll be so much in demand that you might see two beautiful ladies slug it out for your attention.

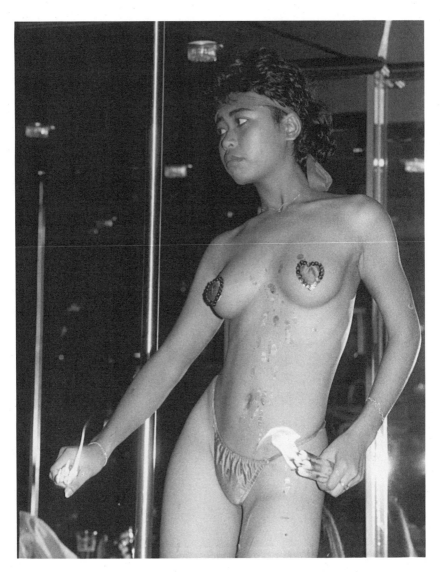

The Fire Dance.

Chapter 16

THE LAST DAYS

I went to Pattaya for a few days to cool out after writing my impressions of Bangkok. When I got back, Pidang had a lot of questions about what I had done there. How many women was I with short-time? How come I spent so much money? And who was Father Tony of the Redemption Center — did he go short-time too? Father Tony Sirichai, I explained, was a Catholic Redemptionist priest who ran a drop-in center for the women who work the bars in Pattaya. Nothing radical, just a place to come and sit, talk or be silent. An important place, especially for some of the younger girls who come from the poverty-stricken northeast and might change their minds about the work once they get a closer look. He could provide a place for them to stay for a few days and even the train fare home if they decided they wanted to leave. He told me he's not out to change the world. No lectures about standing in the flames of hell. More like practical advice: if they're going to stand in hell, how to get the right price for it.

As the days went by and my departure grew near, Pidang and I were more and more like two old friends — closer and closer. When the day of my departure arrived and we went out to the airport, she looked so sad. I told her so, and she just looked at me with her warm loving eyes. She looked radiant in her new white blouse and the pleated mauve-colored skirt I'd bought her.

"I see you over there when you come back," she said, pointing to the arrival area. "You write me before you come, OK? But I have no photo of you!"

"For your file, so that you recognize me when I come back," I said, laughing. (Some of the girls keep files of photos of their men, to make sure they recognize a lover at the airport when he returns.)

"You have all my money," I smiled. *Farang ma mi sathang - mi di bi ban.* "Foreigner no have money, no good, go home."

"Not true," she says. *Farang tha loa* — "Foreigners tell lies."

I kissed her goodbye. Right there in the airport. "Not very Thai," I joked.

"Mi be li," she said, smiling sadly — "Never mind. I'm your wife in Bangkok."

A little girl plays with her rabbit on the streets of Bangkok.